KNOW YOUR TEST METERS
(VOM — VTVM)

KNOW YOUR TEST METERS (VOM — VTVM)

by

Joseph A. Risse

*With a specially written chapter for
the guidance of the English reader
by W. Oliver (G3XT)*

FOULSHAM-SAMS

TECHNICAL BOOKS

Published and distributed by

W. FOULSHAM & CO. LTD.

SLOUGH   BUCKS   ENGLAND

W. FOULSHAM & CO. LTD.

Yeovil Road, Slough, Bucks, England.

KNOW YOUR TEST METERS
(VOM-VTVM)

Introduction Printed and Made in Great Britain
by East Midland Printing Company Limited, Bury St. Edmunds.
Balance printed in U.S.A.

This book sets out to cover wider ground than is usually attempted in the majority of books on the use of electronic test instruments.

In fact, almost everything you need to know about the design, construction, use and maintenance of testmeters can be found somewhere in these pages.

The two classes of meter with which this book is concerned are known by several different names or abbreviations. The simpler of the two is variously called a multi-range testmeter, multimeter, volt-ohm-milliammeter or VOM for short. The more complex one is a valve-voltmeter, vacuum-tube voltmeter (abbreviated to VTVM) or transistorized electronic voltmeter. VOM and VTVM are the abbreviations used mainly in the United States to describe these instruments.

These ever-ready testers help to maintain and repair all kinds of electronic equipment. In return for such faithful service, they certainly deserve a fair share of care and maintenance themselves; therefore this book tells not only what these meters can do but what one can do for them.

Unless you look after a meter properly you cannot expect it to remain 100% accurate, reliable and efficient. If test equipment is to give of its best in helping to maintain or repair other equipment, it must occasionally be overhauled itself.

This is one of the tasks which the present book will help you to carry out efficiently; considerable portions of the text and a good many of the illustrations are devoted to explaining how these test meters are constructed, how they work and how to take care of them so as to ensure their continued accuracy and efficiency.

Where meter maintenance is concerned, however, a word of warning is necessary. It is essential to use a good deal of discretion in regard to which jobs you can safely tackle yourself and which should be left to a meter specialist. Although ruggedly constructed up to a point, a test meter *is* a delicate instrument, and some of the repairs and adjustments that may be called for from time to time are most definitely outside the scope of anyone who is not qualified to handle the delicate, high-precision manipulation required.

The purely electrical part of the assembly should be well within the capabilities of any reasonably skilled technician to overhaul successfully; it is what might be termed the "watchmaker's-type" jobs involving the delicate mechanical movement which are apt to be too tricky to be attempted by anyone who is not a specialist.

If this part of the assembly goes wrong, the proper course is to return the instrument to the maker's service department; or, alternatively, to a fully competent firm specializing in meter overhauls. (It is usually wise to obtain an estimate of the cost of overhaul before requesting repair, as in some cases the job may be pretty costly and if the meter is a fairly old one you may prefer to consider replacing it with a more up-to-date version).

The equipment shown in the photographic illustrations to this book is of American manufacture, since the book itself is of American origin. Actually, a good many American-made meters are available in this country; and many items of American-made ex-Government surplus electronic gear on sale over here contained milliammeters, voltmeters, etc. Many are the home-built testmeters that have been constructed around an American "surplus" milliammeter which formed the "heart" of the instrument.

In any case, the information in this book applies, in most cases, to the British-made equivalents of the various test gear shown. Nearly every kind of American tester has a British-made counterpart which works on similar principles.

This book contains one or two references to 117 volts AC and 60 cps. These, of course, relate to the American standard mains supply, which is quite different from ours in Britain.

110-120 VAC at 60 cycles per second is the usual rating of domestic mains in America, whereas our British mains are rated at about double this voltage, 230-240 VAC at 50 cps being usual in the majority of places nowadays (with a few local exceptions).

While on the subject of voltages, a few words about safety precautions may be opportune. In making tests or taking readings with a meter on any part of a circuit where there are— or, under fault conditions, *may* be—dangerously high voltages, one should be constantly on one's guard against risk of electric shock.

Remember that the practice of holding a test probe in each hand is a potentially dangerous one. It is far safer to have one probe terminated in a crododile clip which can be clipped on to one test-point of the apparatus, and thus leave only one probe that has to be handled. One's free hand can then be kept right away from the apparatus. This avoids the risk of current passing right through one's body, from hand to hand, in the event of accidental contact with two metal points at widely different voltage or potential.

All other necessary safety precautions should also be taken when dealing with any mains-powered sets or equipment.

As already pointed out, this book covers all the essential facts about testmeters—how they are made, how they work, how to take care of them and how to use them. But of course in a volume of this size, covering so much ground in regard to the various aspects of testmeter design, construction, maintenance, etc., it is impossible to go into great detail about *all* the tests and measurements that can be made with such tremendously versatile instruments as the VOM and VTVM. There are, however, other books in the Foulsham-Sams list which are specially devoted to describing in detail the hundreds of different test procedures which can be carried out.

Preface

The volt-ohm-milliammeter and vacuum-tube voltmeter are the most widely used test instruments in modern electrical and electronics work. Because of their widespread applications, a thorough knowledge of the principles of operation, care, and maintenance is important.

Intended for the beginner as well as the experienced user who wishes to know more about VOM's and VTVM's, this book contains all the information necessary for understanding these units. Included are discussions of circuits, the use of the instruments, and how to care for and repair them. Detailed and comprehensive in scope, the units described encompass special-purpose, combination, laboratory, and precision types, as well as transistorized instruments.

The topics discussed concern the VOM's and VTVM's in widest use, in addition to those having special features of particular interest. Extra emphasis is given to the major features common to the most recent models. Procedures for making tests on circuits are included; however, the main subjects considered are the theory of operation and design of the instrument.

The coverage is practical and simple, using very little mathematics. A short review of electrical principles pertinent to AC and DC voltages, current, and resistance measurements is included. This section makes the book of particular interest to students, hobbyists, and others who may need an understanding of the basic principles of voltage or current measuring instruments.

The author wishes to express his thanks to the International Correspondence Schools for the use of their extensive library and laboratory facilities, and to Purcell's Radio and TV Supply for the loan of several instruments. Finally, thanks are due to the many manufacturers who provided detailed information on their products.

June, 1963

JOSEPH A. RISSE

Dedicated to my parents

Joseph P. and Teresa A. Risse

Contents

Chapter 1

Uses of VOM's
and VTVM's

The most widely used test instrument in electrical and electronics work is the VOM (volt-ohm-milliammeter). This instrument is used by scientists, physicists, engineers, technicians, electrical experimenters, teachers, inventors, hobbyists, and students. VOM's are valuable to schools, labs, science, industry, servicing and troubleshooting, electrical maintenance, designing, production and processing. Vacuum-tube voltmeters (VTVM's) are not as widely used as VOM's but, sooner or later, practically every worker in electronics and electricity acquires a VTVM.

OBJECTIVE OF THIS BOOK

Because they are so widely used, a good knowledge of VOM's and VTVM's, the principles of operation, care, and maintenance are important. It is not difficult to learn how to use a VOM or a VTVM. It takes only a few minutes of reading or study of the particular instrument.

The topics discussed in this book are concerned with the VOM's and VTVM's in widest use and with those having features of particular interest. Since it is impossible to discuss every important instrument in this book, a reference to a specific model does not necessarily indicate that this is the only one, or the best. Also, although an attempt was made to consider the most recent models, the latest models are generally the same, though with minor improvements, as earlier versions of the same instrument.

However, the purpose of this book is not to discuss particular instruments. This book discusses the major features common to these instruments. It will tell you what features should be considered before purchasing a new instrument, or how you can best use the one you have.

Widespread Use of The VOM

Your interest in a book of this nature is some indication that you might already know a little about VOM's and how they are used. In electrical and electronics work, the VOM is the tool most frequently used by the technician for servicing, troubleshooting, installation, or maintenance jobs. It is the instrument likely to be closest at hand on the table or workbench.

VOM's are found in many unexpected places. For example, electrical and electronics technicians in an industrial canning plant use VOM's in their work on automated canning machines. Instrument technicians who install and check aircraft instruments use VOM's to trace wiring, measure voltages, and so on. In the plant of a paper manufacturer, technicians use VOM's in adjusting and troubleshooting electronically-controlled machines that roll, cut, inspect, measure, and monitor the color of paper. In gear manufacturing plants, VOM's are used in servicing induction heating equipment that is used in surface-hardening of gears, and crankshafts. At oil refineries, technicians use VOM's in maintaining electronic and microwave equipment used to control the rate-of-flow, mixture, and other operations in the production of oil, gasoline, asphalt, and other products. In a packaging plant, these meters are used in working on ultrasonic equipment whose function is to generate sound and ultrasonic waves that are applied to heat-seal plastic film. These applications, and many more, are in addition to the universal use of VOM's in communications.

What A VOM Can Do

The designers and manufacturers of VOM's try to make them as versatile and convenient to use as possible. The VOM is a single-package instrument with which can be measured voltage, current, and resistance. The ease with which the instrument can be used is usually very important. So, also, is the accuracy of the instrument and the ranges of measurement of which it is capable.

The basic design of the VOM is shown in Fig. 1-1. The meter is the major part of the VOM. The pointer of the meter indicates the value of the voltage, current, or resistance being measured. The voltage measuring section provides for both AC (alternating current) and DC (direct current) voltage measurement over any one of several ranges. In most VOM's there are provisions for measuring direct current but not alternating current, for reasons that will be explained later. The resistance-measuring circuit has several ranges of measurement. In Fig. 1-1, terminal C is common for all measurements; the unknown voltage is connected between E and C, the unknown current between I and C, and the unknown resistance between R and C.

Generally, a VOM provides for a means of measuring voltages up to about 5,000 or 6,000 volts AC or DC, up to about 5, 10, or 15 amperes of current and up to about 1 to 10 megohms resistance. With some VOM's it is also possible to measure decibels and power.

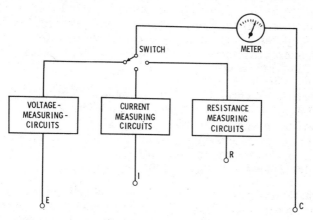

Fig. 1-1. Basic plan of VOM.

At this point, before beginning with detailed discussions about VOM's, it might be worthwhile to review some of the principles of electricity—especially those principles that are important in understanding VOM's and VTVM's.

REVIEW OF ELECTRICITY

You are probably well aware that all matter is composed of molecules, which are made up of atoms. The atoms consist of neutrons, protons, and electrons. The theory that electricity is the flow of electrons through a conductor (such as a wire) is now pretty well established. Electrons are negative charges of electricity. They are repelled by other negative charges of electricity, and they are attracted to or toward positive electrical charges.

9

Current

A movement of electrons constitutes an electrical current. The number of electrons that move during a given period of time determines just how much current is flowing. Current is measured in amperes. Currents less than 1 ampere are generally measured in milliamperes or microamperes. The conversion between amperes (abbreviated amp), milliamperes (abbreviated ma), and microamperes (abbreviated μa) is rather simple; 1 ampere equals 1,000 milliamperes or 1,000,000 microamperes. To convert from:

Amperes to milliamperes multiply amperes $\times$ 1,000
Amperes to microamperes, multiply amperes $\times$ 1,000,000
Milliamperes to amperes, divide milliamperes by 1,000
Microamperes to amperes, divide microamperes by 1,000,000
Microamperes to ma, divide microamperes by 1,000
Milliamperes to microamperes, multiply milliamperes $\times$ 1,000

Example:
Converting amperes to milliamperes—
0.0001 ampere = 0.0001 $\times$ 1,000 = 0.1 milliampere
Converting amperes to microamperes—
0.0001 amperes = 0.0001 $\times$ 1,000,000 = 100 microamperes
Converting milliamperes to amperes—
0.1 milliamperes $\div$ 1,000 = 0.0001 ampere

In practical situations, the units are seldom converted. Instead, the most convenient unit for the amount of current is used. For example, 10 amperes is preferred to 10,000 milliamperes or 10,000,000 microamperes. Similarly, 5 milliamperes rather than 0.005 amperes is preferred.

DC and AC Voltage

Voltage is the energy that causes electrons to move. Usually the source of voltage is a battery or an electric generator. There are two basic kinds of voltage; one is DC voltage, and the other is AC voltage.

DC voltage causes the electrons to move from the negative side of the voltage source, through one of the two wires required, through the circuit being powered, to the second wire back to the positive side of the voltage source. An example of such a DC circuit, a battery providing the power for a lamp bulb, is shown in Fig. 1-2.

The movement of electrons is continuous from negative to positive, until the voltage is removed by opening the circuit.

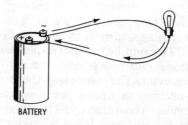

Fig. 1-2. Direct current circuit.

BATTERY

AC voltage also causes electrons to move from negative to positive. The difference between AC and DC voltage, however, is that the AC polarity keeps changing at a regular rate, as does the amplitude (magnitude) of the voltage. At first, one of the two terminals of the AC voltage source is negative and the other positive, as shown for terminals A and B in Fig. 1-3A; then the one that was negative becomes positive, and the one that was positive becomes negative, as in Fig. 1-3B. The positive side starts from zero voltage (point 1 in Fig. 1-3C), builds up to a maximum positive value (point 2), then decreases to zero again (point 3), then builds up to the maximum negative value (point 4), then back to zero (point 5), to maximum positive (point 6). This is then repeated. The result is

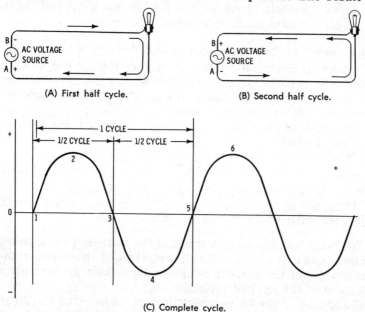

(A) First half cycle.

(B) Second half cycle.

(C) Complete cycle.

Fig. 1-3. Alternating directions of electron flow through circuit connected to AC voltage source.

that the electrons flow through the wire first in one direction, then stop, and reverse or flow in the other direction, then reverse again, until the circuit is opened.

The number of times per second that a pair of these variations (zero to positive to zero to negative to zero) occurs is known as the *frequency* of the AC voltage. Frequency is usually specified in cycles per second (cps) or sometimes simply as cycles. The value of AC voltage supplied by the utility company to the average home is about 117 volts, and its frequency is usually 60 cps.

Resistance

The opposition to the flow of electrons through a material is known as resistance. Resistance is low through a wire and through most metals and other conductors. Through nonconductors, or insulators, resistance is high. Resistance is measured in ohms.

Some components in electrical circuits consist of materials designed to have a specific value of resistance; these components, known as resistors, are available in many sizes and values of resistance. The amount of current a resistor must carry usually determines its physical size. Conductors, such as wires, generally have a low resistance—a typical figure would be 1 to 10 ohms for a 100-foot piece of wire.

Relationship of Voltage, Current, and Resistance

In a given electrical circuit, the higher the applied voltage, the greater the amount of current flow; the lower the voltage the less the current. Similarly, the greater the resistance, the lower the current and vice versa.

The relationship of current, voltage, and resistance is given by Ohm's law as:

$$E = IR$$

where,
E is the value of the applied voltage, in volts,
I is the amount of current, in amperes, flowing in the circuit,
R is the value of the resistance, in ohms.

The preceding equation states that the voltage is equal to the current multiplied by the resistance. Thus, if the value of the resistance and the current is known then their product gives the value of the applied voltage.

If any two of the three quantities are known, the third can be determined. For instance, if the voltage and current are known, the equation for determining the resistance is:

$$R = \frac{E}{I}$$

Or, resistance is equal to voltage divided by current.

And, if the resistance and the voltage are known, the equation for the current is:

$$I = \frac{E}{R}$$

Or, current is equal to voltage divided by resistance.

Power

The amount of power absorbed in an electrical circuit is usually stated in watts. The power in watts can be found from the equation:

$$P = I^2R$$

where,

P is the power in watts.

Or, the power equals the value of the current squared times the resistance.

The power can also be found if the current and voltage are known:

$$P = EI$$

Or, if the voltage and the resistance are known:

$$P = \frac{E^2}{R}$$

In many cases it is important to use an electrical component that is large enough in physical size to dissipate the heat due to the flow of electrical current through the component. Therefore resistors have a rating in watts. Resistors are commercially available in ⅛, ¼, ½, 1, 2, 5, 10, 25, 50, . . .—watt sizes. In designing circuits, usually a resistor having twice the wattage rating needed is selected. This is to allow for the possibility that the resistor will operate at a higher temperature than calculations would indicate, due to its location beneath a chassis or inside a cabinet, where the heat is not readily carried away by convection, conduction, or radiation.

Suppose that in a circuit with a voltage source of 100 volts, 0.005 amperes of current flow is required. The value of the desired resistor is determined from the equation given earlier:

$$R = \frac{E}{I} = \frac{100}{.005} = 20,000 \text{ ohms}$$

13

Next, to determine its rating in watts, use the formula:

$$P = EI = 100 \times .005 = 0.5 \text{ watts}$$

Using either formula $P = EI$ or $P = I^2R$ would have given the same answer.

In an open space a ½ watt resistor could be used, but if the circuit is enclosed, or the escape of heat is restricted in any manner, a 1-watt resistor would be used.

Characteristics of Alternating Current

The electrical principles and laws just given for DC apply equally to AC. That is, 100 volts AC will cause 0.005 ampere to flow through 20,000 ohms the same as 100 volts DC.

It is important, however, to realize the important characteristics of AC. Since it ranges from zero to maximum positive to maximum negative for each cycle, its average value for each cycle is zero. Of course, as far as its effect in an electrical circuit is concerned, this average value of zero does not mean that it has no effect. An AC voltage, in forcing electrons through a circuit first in one direction and then in the other, creates heat, or causes other effects just as does DC voltage. However, the effective value of alternating current is not actually its maximum value. The effective value of AC is related to its maximum value by the factor 0.707, as is indicated in Fig. 1-4.

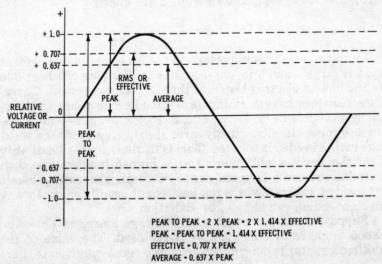

PEAK TO PEAK = 2 X PEAK = 2 X 1.414 X EFFECTIVE
PEAK = PEAK TO PEAK = 1.414 X EFFECTIVE
EFFECTIVE = 0.707 X PEAK
AVERAGE = 0.637 X PEAK

Fig. 1-4. Relationship between peak-to-peak, peak, effective, and average values of voltage or current.

$$E \text{ (AC effective)} = E \text{ (AC maximum)} \times 0.707$$
$$I \text{ (AC effective)} = I \text{ (AC maximum)} \times 0.707$$

The relationship in the other direction, maximum to effective, is by the factor 1.414.

$$\text{Maximum} = \text{Effective} \times 1.414$$

Thus, as an example, an AC voltage having a value of 150 volts for its positive and negative peaks has an effective value of:

$$150 \times 0.707 = 106 \text{ volts, (approximately)}.$$

An AC voltage having an effective value of 110 volts has a maximum value of:

$$110 \times 1.414 = 155.5 \text{ volts, (approximately)}.$$

Another term frequently used for maximum values is peak value; and another term commonly used for effective value is rms (root-mean-square) value.

The value of an AC voltage or current is sometimes given in terms of its peak-to-peak value. It is obvious that the peak-to-peak value of a symmetrical AC wave is twice its peak value:

$$\begin{aligned} \text{Peak-to-peak} &= 2 \times \text{peak} \\ &= 2 \times 1.414 \times \text{effective} \\ &= 2.828 \times \text{effective} \end{aligned}$$

Although the average value of a complete AC cycle is zero, each half cycle of an AC wave has a specific average value. The average value of a half cycle of AC is given by:

$$\text{Average} = 0.637 \times \text{peak}$$

For many practical purposes AC voltage or current is referred to as having an average value of 0.637 times its peak value, not necessarily restricting the designation to applying to only a half cycle at a time; but for other purposes it is important to keep in mind that the average value of an AC sine-wave voltage or current is zero. This will become apparent later, when meter movements are discussed.

Chapter 2

VOM's

The basic components of the VOM, as shown in Fig. 2-1, are a meter, test leads, a function switch and voltage-, current-, and resistance-measuring circuits.

BASIC VOM SYSTEM

In some VOM's the switch is not included—in this case, it is necessary to move one of the test leads each time a different function is to be performed by the meter. In Fig. 2-1, if there were no switch, the right-hand test lead would be left where it is at all times, and the left-hand lead would be plugged into

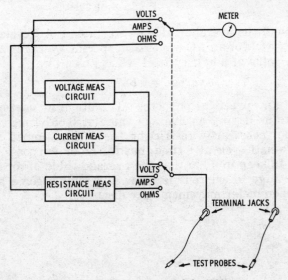

Fig. 2-1. Basic components of the VOM.

Fig. 2-2. Triplett Model 630 VOM.

Courtesy Triplett Electrical Instrument Co.

a jack connecting to the resistance-, current-, or voltage-measuring network, as desired. Most VOM's do include the function switch, however, and for this reason it is shown here. In some VOM's that include the function switch, one test lead is still moved to a different jack when the type of measurement being made is changed. An example of one such VOM is shown in Fig. 2-2. The large switch knob located at the lower center is used to select any one of several ranges of AC or DC voltage, DC current, or ohms.

To understand the VOM—what it is, how it works, and how to use and care for it—it is necessary first to understand its components. The first one to consider is the meter.

Meter of VOM

The meter includes the pointer or indicator that is attached to a mechanism called a *movement*. When the VOM is not being used, the pointer remains at the O-side of the calibrated scale of the meter as in Fig. 2-2. When current flows through the movement, the pointer moves to some position and remains there, if the flow of current is steady, until the current changes in value. Just how much the pointer is moved or deflected, depends on how much current is flowing through the movement.

It should be kept in mind that whether it is voltage, current, or resistance being measured, it is always current that deflects the pointer.

Principle of Meter Movement

The type of meter movement used in most VOM's is known as the d'Arsonval movement. This movement includes a perma-

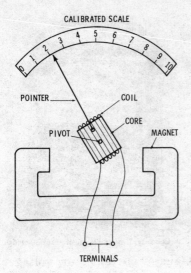

CALIBRATED SCALE

POINTER

COIL

CORE

PIVOT

MAGNET

TERMINALS

Fig. 2-3. Principle of the d'Arsonval
movement.

nent magnet and a coil to which a pointer is attached, which rotates in the field of the magnet when current passes through the turns of the coil. The principle of the d'Arsonval movement is shown in Fig. 2-3. The coil is wound about a soft iron core. The current to be measured flows through the coil, setting up a magnetic field around the coil, which opposes the field of the magnet. The coil is rotated clockwise by these repelling fields, pulling against a spring which, when no current is passing through the coil, holds the pointer at zero on the calibrated scale. The greater the current is, the greater is the force turning the coil.

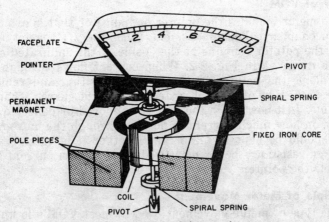

FACEPLATE

POINTER

PERMANENT
MAGNET

POLE PIECES

PIVOT

SPIRAL SPRING

FIXED IRON CORE

COIL

PIVOT

SPIRAL SPRING

Fig. 2-4. Construction details of d'Arsonval movements.

The basic construction details of the d'Arsonval movement are shown more clearly in Fig. 2-4. Pole pieces on the permanent magnet decrease the magnetic gap between the magnet and the coil core. Spiral springs hold the pointer, which is fastened to the coil, at zero when no current is flowing. The core of the coil does not rotate; it is stationary in order to keep the pointer assembly as light in weight as possible. The pivot usually rides in jewel bearings to reduce friction.

Example of Meter Movement

If anything goes wrong with a meter movement, it is usually necessary to return it to the manufacturer for repair. It is seldom possible for anyone other than a specialist who is skilled in the repair and adjustment of meters to properly repair a meter movement. Many technicians have learned this the hard way. Repair attempts by a novice or even a technician are not practical; this should be obvious, if the assembly details of a typical meter movement are noted (Fig. 2-5). The assembled unit is shown in Fig. 2-5A and the motor portion (the part that includes the coil, core, jewels, spiral springs, pointer, etc.) is shown in Fig. 2-5B. An exploded view of the motor is shown in Fig. 2-5C. Note that the coil is referred to as the armature and that the spiral springs are attached to it. Also notice that to make the motor assembly as precise as possible, the pole pieces are made a part of it. The zero-adjust arm, which is part of the top bridge, is the only adjustment of the movement which the user of the VOM should make. It is usually set by turning an eccentric screw on the outside of the meter case so that the pointer indicates zero when no current is flowing through the movement. The internal zero adjust is a factory adjustment. Not all meter movements are as elaborate as that shown in Fig. 2-5, but this is an example of a movement used in several high quality VOM's. The pointer of a meter of this type will be deflected to its full-scale position when a 50-microampere current (0.00005 ampere) flows through the coil. According to one manufacturer, this 50 microamperes is obtained when 250 millivolts is applied to the meter terminals; hence, the resistance of the movement is:

$$R = \frac{E}{I} = \frac{0.25}{0.00005} = 5,000 \text{ ohms}$$

The less current required to deflect a meter full-scale, the more sensitive the meter is said to be. Some meter movements will deflect full scale with even less than 50 microamperes; many require a higher current.

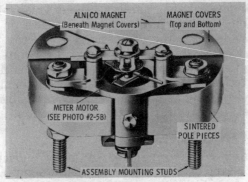

ALNICO MAGNET
(Beneath Magnet Covers)

MAGNET COVERS
(Top and Bottom)

METER MOTOR
(SEE PHOTO #2-5B)

SINTERED
POLE PIECES

ASSEMBLY MOUNTING STUDS

(A) Movement assembled.

(B) Motor section of movement assembled.

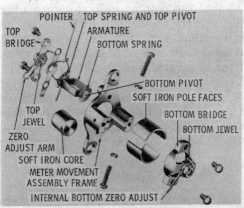

POINTER   TOP SPRING AND TOP PIVOT

TOP
BRIDGE

ARMATURE

BOTTOM SPRING

BOTTOM PIVOT
SOFT IRON POLE FACES

BOTTOM BRIDGE

BOTTOM JEWEL

TOP
JEWEL

ZERO
ADJUST ARM

SOFT IRON CORE

METER MOVEMENT
ASSEMBLY FRAME

INTERNAL BOTTOM ZERO ADJUST

(C) Exploded view, motor section.

Courtesy Pace Electrical Instrument Co.

Fig. 2-5. Example of a typical d'Arsonval meter movement.

CURRENT-MEASURING CIRCUIT

If it is desired to use a meter movement alone to measure current in a circuit, it may be done if the amount of current flowing does not exceed the rated current of the meter movement. To illustrate, a 50-microampere meter in the circuit of Fig. 2-6A will be deflected to ½-scale. Thirty volts applied to 1,200,000 ohms (the 1,195,000 ohm resistor and the

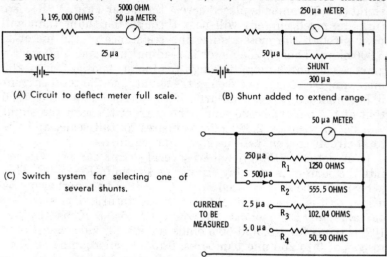

(A) Circuit to deflect meter full scale.

(B) Shunt added to extend range.

(C) Switch system for selecting one of several shunts.

Fig. 2-6. Method of using meter for current measurements.

5,000 ohms of the meter movement) causes 25 microamperes to flow through the meter. This is expressed as:

$$I = \frac{E}{R} = \frac{30}{1,200,000} = 25 \text{ microamperes}$$

If the battery should be reduced to 15 volts, the meter will be deflected to ¼-full scale; if it is reduced to 7.5 volts the meter will deflect to ⅛ its full-scale reading. This process can be continued until the voltage applied will become so low that the movement of the pointer will no longer be discernible. The lowest voltage at which the movement of the meter is no longer significant will be the lower limit of usefulness of the meter. The upper limit of usefulness of the meter is, of course, the point where the battery voltage exceeds 60 volts, since beyond this voltage level the current flowing in the circuit will exceed the maximum rating of the meter. Permitting too much current to flow through a meter can cause the coil to burn out, or the meter to be otherwise damaged.

Extending Current Range of Meter Movement

The meter in the circuit of Fig. 2-6A can be used to measure currents greater than 50 microamperes. To do this a shunt or path is provided around the meter to carry a known portion of the current, so that the current through the meter is 50 microamperes or less. This shunt is a resistor as shown in Fig. 2-6B, whose value must be accurately selected. For example, if a shunt of 1,000 ohms is placed across the meter (Fig. 2-6B), five times as much current will pass through the shunt than will pass through the meter, since the resistance of the meter is 5,000 ohms. Thus, if the meter is reading full-scale, a 50 microampere current is going through the meter, and 50 × 5 or 250 microamperes is going through the shunt, and the total current is 300 microamperes. Similarly, if the shunt has a value 1/50 that of the meter or 100 ohms, the current through the shunt will be 50 × 50 or 2,500 microamperes at full scale, and the total circuit current will be 2,550 microamperes.

In an actual VOM any one of several shunts can be switched into the current measuring circuit, as shown in Fig. 2-6C. This is basically the scheme used in the VOM that you might now be using, or the one you might use in the future. The selection of values of 1,250 ohms for shunt R1, 555.5 ohms for R2, 102.04 ohms for R3, and 50.5 ohms for R4, provides additional ranges of 0 to 250 microamperes, 0 to 500 microamperes, 0 to 2.5 milliamperes and 0 to 5.0 milliamperes respectively. In many practical VOM's the shunt switching arrangement makes it possible to measure DC currents as high as 10, 12, or 15 amps or more. For these higher ranges, the shunts are actual pieces of wire or strap whose resistances are accurately selected.

DC VOLTAGE MEASURING CIRCUIT

If 250 millivolts are applied to the terminals of a 50-microampere meter movement having a resistance of 5,000 ohms, the meter will deflect full scale. The meter could be used by itself to measure voltages up to 250 millivolts. If a voltage is applied to the meter terminals and the pointer deflects to its halfway point, it can be assumed that the voltage has a value of 125 millivolts.

Of course, with a typical VOM it is possible to measure voltages much greater than 250 millivolts. Extending the voltage-measuring capability of a meter movement is made possible by adding a multiplier resistor in series with the meter. In

Fig. 2-7A, the multiplier resistor shown has a value of 15,000 ohms. This added to the 5,000 ohms of the meter totals 20,000 ohms. Since the meter requires 50 microamperes for full scale deflection, it can easily be determined that the voltage required to provide this full scale deflection is:

$$E = I \times R = 0.00005 \times 20,000 = 1 \text{ volt}$$

Thus, with the 15,000 ohm multiplier, a meter circuit capable of measuring up to 1 volt full scale is obtained. To add a range for measuring up to 10 volts, the total resistance of the circuit must be increased 10 times, or to 200,000 ohms. The value of the multiplier then would be 200,000 − 5,000, or 195,000 ohms. Similarly, for a 100-volt full scale range, the multiplier must have a value of 2,000,000 − 5,000, or 1,995,000 ohms. A switch is normally used, as in Fig. 2-7B, for selecting the desired full-scale voltage ranges of 1 volt, 10 volts, or 100 volts.

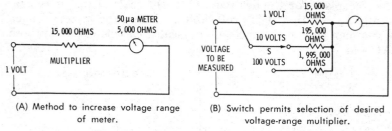

(A) Method to increase voltage range of meter.

(B) Switch permits selection of desired voltage-range multiplier.

Fig. 2-7. Basic VOM voltage measuring circuit.

In a practical VOM, series multiplier-resistors are used to make it possible to measure voltages up to 5,000 or 6,000 DC volts or more. Measurement of voltages even higher than this is possible, but usually this is not provided in a VOM because of the danger of breakdown of components, arc-over between components and wiring, and danger to the user. The range of a VOM can be increased to measure higher voltages by use of a high-voltage probe, as will be explained later in this book.

CIRCUIT FOR MEASUREMENT OF AC VOLTAGE

In a VOM, the basic circuit generally used for measuring AC voltage is essentially the same as that for measuring DC voltage. The main difference is that, for AC voltage measurement, a rectifier is included in the circuit.

The rectifier may be either a half-wave rectifier as in Fig. 2-8A or a full-wave rectifier. Often a bridge circuit is used as in Fig. 2-8B or a double half-wave rectifier as in Fig. 2-8C. Usually, but not always, a copper oxide rectifier is employed, rather than the selenium, silicon, germanium, or vacuum-tube types.

A rectifier permits current flow almost entirely in one direction only. Therefore it changes the AC voltage to be measured to a DC voltage in the form of a series of half sine-waves. Thus, current flows through the d'Arsonval meter in one direction only, just as for DC measurement.

Because of the additional resistance of the rectifier in the circuit for AC measurement, it is usually necessary for the designer of a VOM to use different multipliers in the AC voltage measuring circuit than those for DC voltage measurement. This would not be necessary if different calibrated scales on the faceplate of the meter were used for DC and AC. However, there would be a possibility of confusion when using a VOM if it were necessary to search through a maze of calibrations on the faceplate for the desired AC or DC scale. Thus, it is generally agreed that it is preferable to design the meter in such a manner that the same voltage scales can be used for both AC and DC.

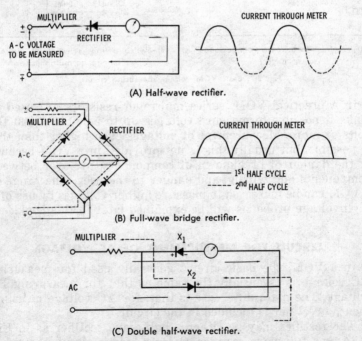

(A) Half-wave rectifier.

(B) Full-wave bridge rectifier.

(C) Double half-wave rectifier.

Fig. 2-8. Basic rectifier circuits used in measurement of AC voltage.

The half-wave rectifier circuit shown in Fig. 2-8A is actually seldom employed in a high quality VOM. The only important reason for this is that copper-oxide and other solid-state rectifiers conduct some current on the negative half-cycles. Assume that a certain copper-oxide rectifier has a resistance of 200 ohms in one direction. This is the direction in which it would best conduct on the positive half-cycles. Then, typically, it would have a resistance of 100,000 ohms in the other direction. On negative half-cycles it would therefore, in most circuits, conduct very little current. But in a VOM circuit, on all but the lowest voltage ranges, the multiplier resistors have fairly high values, and the reverse current may be appreciable compared to the forward current.

To illustrate, in Fig. 2-8A, on the 100-volt range the resistance of the multiplier, rectifier, and meter in the forward direction might be 2,000,200 ohms, and in the reverse direction the resistance might be 2,100,000 ohms. Then on positive half-cycles the current would be very close to 50 microamperes, but on negative half-cycles, instead of the current being practically zero, it would be $\frac{100}{2,100,000}$, or approximately 43 microamperes. The 50 microamperes going through the meter for all the positive half-cycles would tend to deflect the pointer to full scale, and the 43 microamperes going the opposite direction through the meter on negative half-cycles would tend to swing the pointer nearly as much in the other direction. The two opposing forces would be happening only 1/120 of a second apart, so the net effect on the meter reading would be the difference between the forward and reverse currents, or $50 - 43 = 7$ microamperes. Rather than the meter indicating 100 volts then, this 7 microamperes would cause the pointer to indicate 14 volts on the 100-volt scale.

Whenever half-wave rectifier circuits are employed in VOM's they are often the double half-wave type shown in Fig. 2-8C. For this circuit, the overall measuring circuit has approximately the same resistance for both half cycles of measured AC but on the reverse or negative half-cycles, the second rectifier X2 shunts the reverse current around the meter thus preventing it from cancelling out any appreciable part of the forward or positive half-cycles.

BASIC VOM CIRCUITS FOR RESISTANCE MEASUREMENT

The basic circuits used in VOM's for measuring DC current, and DC and AC voltage have been discussed. The remaining major function of a VOM is to measure resistance. Since resistance is measured in ohms, a resistance measuring circuit is called an ohmmeter circuit. There are two types of ohmmeter circuits: the series-ohmmeter circuit and the shunt-ohmmeter circuit. Either one or both may be found in a typical good quality VOM.

The series-ohmmeter circuit includes a source of power (usually a battery), a calibrated meter, a fixed current-limiting resistor, and a variable resistor, as shown in Fig. 2-9. Also, of

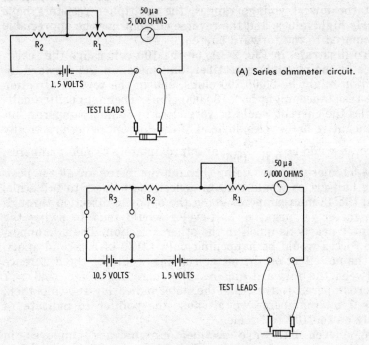

(A) Series ohmmeter circuit.

(B) Circuit for measuring higher resistances.

Fig. 2-9. Resistance measuring circuits.

course, a pair of test leads connects to this resistance measuring circuit.

For the purpose of discussion here, assume that a 50 microampere meter having a resistance of 5,000 ohms is used, that the value of the current limiting resistor R2 is 22,000 ohms, that R1 is a 0-5,000 ohm potentiometer adjusted to a value of 3,000 ohms, and that the battery is 1.5 volts. With a total resistance of 30,000 ohms, and with 1.5 volts applied to the circuit, if the resistance being measured is zero ohms, the circuit current should be exactly the 50 microamperes required by the meter to read full scale. In fact, this is essentially how an ohmmeter is calibrated for zero ohms. The tips of the test probes are held together, and the variable resistor is adjusted until the meter reads exactly full scale, corresponding to zero ohms. Now, if the test probes are placed across the terminals of a resistor with a higher value than zero ohms, the deflection of the meter will be less than zero ohms on the scale. Assume further that the resistance being measured has a value of 30,000 ohms, the same as the measuring circuit. The meter now will be deflected to ½ full-scale value, since with twice the resistance the current will be ½ as great. If the probes are placed across the leads of other resistors whose values are greater or less than 30,000 ohms, the indication will be either below or above the ½-scale reading of the meter, respectively, in proportion to the difference of the resistance value. Thus, the meter faceplate can be calibrated to read various values of resistance.

Theoretically, this circuit will respond to any value of resistance between 0 and infinity. But in practice, with the values suggested here, resistances less than 1,000 ohms and above 500,000 ohms can not be measured accurately. This is because these values of about 1,000 ohms and 500,000 ohms are very small and very large respectively, compared to the measuring circuit total resistance of 30,000 ohms. The 1,000-ohm resistor would cause a deflection of about 97 percent of full scale, and the 500,000-ohm resistor would cause a fairly feeble deflection; neither could be read very accurately.

Circuit For Measuring Higher Resistances

A method of extending the high-end range of an ohmmeter is shown in Fig. 2-9B. A 210,000-ohm resistor and a 10.5-volt battery have been switched into the circuit. With the test leads shorted, the current will be:

$$\frac{(10.5 + 1.5) \text{ volts}}{(210,000 + 22,000 + 3,000 + 5,000)} = \frac{12}{240,000}$$
$$= 50 \text{ microamperes}$$

This is the current required for full-scale deflection. However, at the mid-range point on the scale 240,000 ohms can be read compared to 30,000 ohms for the 1.5-volt battery and 30,000-ohm total circuit resistance in the first example. Furthermore, assuming accurate reading down to the 10 percent deflection point of 5 microamperes on the meter, it will be possible to measure resistance up to:

$$\frac{12}{5 \times 10^{-6}} - 30{,}000 = 2{,}400{,}000 - 30{,}000 = 2{,}370{,}000 \text{ ohms}$$

or about 2.5 megohms. With the beginning circuit of the 1.5-volt battery and 30,000 ohms circuit resistance, the 10 percent deflection point reading would be:

$$300{,}000 - 30{,}000 = 270{,}000 \text{ ohms}$$

Circuit For Measuring Lower Resistances

It was shown that the circuit in Fig. 2-9A was not satisfactory for measuring low values of resistance. Of course, the circuit in Fig. 2-9B is even less suitable. In commercial ohmmeter circuits, the very low values of resistance are measured by use of the shunt ohmmeter circuit shown in Fig. 2-10. The test leads in the measuring circuit now connect across the meter. When the test probes are connected across an unkown value of resistance, the current in the measuring circuit is reduced, part of it going through the meter and part through the unknown resistance. Call the resistance 5,000 ohms, thereby reducing the equivalent resistance across the points A and B to 2,500 ohms. Although the total current in the circuit increases now to $\frac{1.5}{27{,}500}$, or about 55 microamperes the current through the meter itself is half that amount, or about 27.5 microamperes. Thus, measuring a resistance of 5,000 ohms would give an indication on the scale at slightly above mid-range. Further variations of the shunt ohmmeter circuit of Fig. 2-10 will permit reading even lower values of resistance. In some VOM's, for certain ranges of resistance measurement, a combination of a series circuit and the shunt circuit is employed.

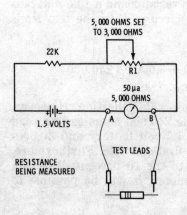

Fig. 2-10. Shunt ohmmeter circuit for measuring low values of resistance.

MULTIPLE USE OF SCALES IN TYPICAL VOM

In a commercial VOM the multiplier and shunt resistances for different ranges of voltage, current, and resistance measurement are chosen so that the range-selecting switch can be labelled logically, and so that the calibrated scales on the meter faceplate can present several ranges.

For example, for the VOM shown in Fig. 2-11, the calibrated scale, second from the top of the faceplate, and labelled, 0, 30, 60, 90, 120, and 150 can be used for reading currents up to 1.5 milliamperes, 15 milliamperes, 150 milliamperes, 1.5 am-

Fig. 2-11. Typical VOM showing faceplate
and range-selector switch labelling.

Courtesy Pacotronics Incorporated

peres, or 15 amperes, respectively, in accordance with the setting of the range switch (lower right). The same scale can be used for DC voltages on the 1.5-volt and 150-volt ranges.

The third scale from the top, marked 0, 5, 10, etc., up to 30, and 1, 2, 3, etc., to 6, is used for reading voltages between 0 and 30 volts DC, 0 to 6 volts DC, 0 to 600 volts DC or 0 to 6,000 volts DC.

The third scale (from the top) having maximum markings of 300, 60, and 12 is used for AC voltage measurements on the ranges 0 to 12, 0 to 60, 0 to 300, 0 to 1200, and 0 to 12,000-volts AC. A separate range, next to the bottom on the faceplate is provided for 0- to 3-volt AC measurements. This separate calibration provides additional accuracy, compensating for the nonlinearity of the rectifier at low AC voltages.

29

The bottom scale, marked DB, is for the measurement of audio-frequency voltages in terms of decibels. The use of a VOM for this purpose will be explained later.

For the measurement of resistance, the top scale is used for all ranges; the range-selection switch is calibrated R × 1, R × 100, and R × 10,000 for resistance measurement. Note that the figure 10 appears at about midrange on the ohms scale. For resistance measurements, if the range switch is set to R × 1, this number 10 indicates 10 ohms; for R × 100 range, the 10 indicates 10 × 100 or 1,000 ohms; and for the R × 10,000 range, the 10 indicates 10 × 10,000 or 100,000. Note that on this highest resistance range it is possible to read resistances accurately up to the point marked 500, or 500 × 10,000 ohms (5 megohms). Low resistance values can be read on the R × 1 scale to well below 1 ohm.

The round knob at the lower center of the meter is the Ohms Adjust control, equivalent to R1 in Figs. 2-9 and 2-10. The knob is used for setting the pointer deflection exactly to full scale when the test probes are shorted together.

OUTPUT MEASUREMENT CIRCUIT

Input and output signals of amplifiers are sometimes measured or specified in watts, sometimes in volts, and sometimes in db (decibels). Where it is desired to measure in volts, the proper AC range of the VOM is used. Assuming that the amplifier is for the audio-frequency range and that the VOM has a good response in this range, the reading obtained will indicate the rms value of the audio voltage.

If power in watts is the desired measurement, the square of the measured voltage (E) is then divided by the resistance (R) of the input or output circuit. That is:

$$\text{Power in watts} = \frac{E^2}{R}$$

As an example, 90 volts AC is measured across an amplifier output circuit impedance of 600 ohms. Then the output power is:

$$P = \frac{90^2}{600} = \frac{8100}{600} = 13.5 \text{ watts}$$

When it is desired to measure output in db, most VOM's include a specially calibrated scale on the meter faceplate, such as the bottom scale on the meter shown in Fig. 2-2. If no DC is present in the AC or audio signal to be measured, one of the

AC facilities of the meter may be used to make the measurement in db. Ordinarily however, a VOM will have a test-lead jack labelled Output, such as the one to the right of the selector knob in Fig. 2-2. One of the test leads is plugged into the Common jack, and the other lead is plugged into this Output jack.

Usually the only circuit difference between the Output jack and the AC jack is that in the Output jack a capacitor is in series with the measuring circuit to isolate the meter circuit from any DC present in the circuit under test.

In the meter of Fig. 2-2 the number of db may be read directly from the DB scale when the range switch is on 3 volts AC. On the faceplate of the meter (lower right corner) is information for interpreting db readings on other AC ranges. For instance, when the 12-volt AC range is used, 12 db is added to the pointer indication; when the 60-volt AC range is used, 26 db is added to the pointer indication, etc.

The db values are usable directly only for measurements on a 600-ohm circuit. Furthermore, the scale is calibrated on the basis that 0 db is equal to 1 milliwatt and only, as mentioned earlier, on a 600-ohm circuit. Db measurements on circuits other than 600 ohms may be made, but then the readings obtained will only be relative. Charts and graphs are available for converting db readings in circuits of various impedances to actual db values with respect to 1 milliwatt taken as the 0 db reference. Often these charts and tables are included in the VOM manufacturer's instruction manual.

SENSITIVITY OF A VOM

One of the most important characteristics of a VOM is its sensitivity rating. This is specified in terms of so many ohms per volt. The higher the ohms-per-volt rating, the more sensitive is the VOM. The sensitivity rating is usually specified on the face of the meter or given in the instruction manual. It can also be determined by using one of the following formulas:

$$\text{Sensitivity (ohms per volt)} = \frac{1}{E_{fs}} \times R_m$$

$$= \frac{1,000,000}{\mu A}$$

where,

E_{fs} is the voltage required for deflecting the meter full scale,
R_m is the resistance of the meter movement,
μA is the current required for full scale deflection of the meter.

The sensitivity may also be determined by dividing the total resistance of the circuit for the range in use by the voltage value of that range. To illustrate, suppose the 0-12–volt DC range is in use, and for this position of the range switch there are 240,000 ohms in the measuring circuit. The sensitivity of the measuring circuit is then:

$$\frac{240,000}{12} = 20,000 \text{ ohms per volt}$$

The same ohms-per-volt rating would apply to all DC ranges of the VOM. For the AC ranges, however, the sensitivity is usually rated lower. The lower rating is due to the leakage resistance of the rectifier in the reverse direction. The sensitivity of the VOM of Fig. 2-2 on the AC ranges is 5,000 ohms per volt. In practice, it is usually important to have a high sensitivity rating on the DC ranges, the AC sensitivity rating not being quite so important. In many applications, however, a VOM having a sensitivity of only 1,000 ohms per volt will be satisfactory. Such a VOM is shown in Fig. 2-12. A 1,000 ohms-per-volt VOM is much less expensive than one of 20,000 ohms per volt, and the measurements made with the less expensive instrument will be just as accurate when these voltage measurements are made across resistances or impedances of relatively low value.

Fig. 2-12. A 1,000 ohms-per-volt VOM.

Courtesy EICO

Loading Effect of Meter

The need for using a high-sensitivity VOM for voltage measurement in high-impedance circuits becomes apparent if the results are examined when one with low-sensitivity is used.

For instance, in the circuit of Fig. 2-13, with 3-volts DC applied across two 10,000-ohm resistors (R1 and R2) in series, the drop across each resistor is 1.5 volts, and the circuit current is:

$$I = \frac{3}{20,000} = 0.00015 \text{ ampere}$$

Now assume the use of the 3-volt range on a 1,000 ohms-per-volt meter to measure the voltage across R1. On the 3-volt range, the total internal resistance of the VOM is only 3,000 ohms.

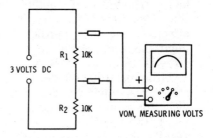

Fig. 2-13. Circuit showing loading effects of VOM.

3 VOLTS DC

R1 10K

R2 10K

VOM, MEASURING VOLTS

As soon as the VOM test leads are connected across R1, the 3,000-ohm resistance of the meter in parallel with the 10,000 ohms of R1 has an effective value of approximately 2,300 ohms, changing the total circuit resistance to 10,000 plus 2,300, or 12,300 ohms.

The circuit current now becomes:

$$I = \frac{3}{12,300} = 0.000243 \text{ ampere}$$

And the voltage drop across the terminals of R1 to which the VOM leads are connected is:

$$E = 2,300 \times 0.000243 = 0.56 \text{ volt}$$

This is the value the meter will read instead of 1.5 volts, which will actually be the voltage across R1 when the VOM is not connected.

The change in circuit conditions caused by connecting a meter to a circuit is called the *loading effect* of the meter. It is apparent that in the example just shown, the loading effect of the 1,000 ohms-per-volt meter was considerable. If now, a 20,000 ohms-per-volt VOM is used to measure the voltage across R1 in Fig. 2-12, the loading effect is considerably less. On the 3-volt range, a 20,000 ohms-per-volt instrument has an internal resistance of 60,000 ohms. This 60,000 ohms across the 10,000 ohms of R1 gives a combined resistance of approximately 8,600 ohms. Then, by calculation as before, the voltage across R1 with the 20,000 ohms-per-volt VOM connected is approximately 1.4 volts. Although this represents an error of about 7 percent, it is a considerable improvement over the reading of .56 volt obtained with the 1,000 ohms-per-volt instrument.

Of course a 1,000 ohms-per-volt VOM does not have a serious loading effect on every circuit. For instance, the use of the 150-volt range to measure 100 volts across a 1,000-ohm resistor would give highly accurate results. The 150-volt range has a resistance of 150,000 ohms. This 150,000 ohms across the 1,000 ohms of the circuit under test would have a negligible effect. Conversely, neither is a 20,000 ohms-per-volt instrument the final answer to measurements in all high-impedance circuits. If such a VOM is used on the 1.5 volt range to measure 1 volt across 100,000 ohms, the loading effect of the 35,000-ohm meter resistance on this range would be quite serious. However, for a high percentage of the measurements in electronics work, the 20,000 ohms-per-volt instrument provides accurate results. For the remaining percentage, either a higher resistance VOM is required, or more often a VTVM is employed. The advantage of the VTVM with respect to circuit loading is considered later in this book.

Higher-Sensitivity VOM's

In the past, meters having a higher sensitivity than 20,000 ohms-per-volt have not been widely employed in routine measurement work, but an increasing number of manufacturers have recently been including at least one in their popular line of meters. An example of a VOM having a sensitivity of 100,000 ohms per volt on the DC ranges is shown in Fig. 2-14. The instrument employs a 10-microampere meter movement. For measuring voltages of 100 volts or more across circuit resistances of 10 megohms or more, a 100,000 ohms-per-volt VOM, such as this one, has even less loading effect than the common VTVM. This high-sensitivity movement is protected from shock, vibration, and overload.

Another VOM having a sensitivity of 100,000 ohms per volt on some DC voltage ranges, and 200,000 ohms per volt on the

Courtesy Simpson Electric Co.

Fig. 2-14. Simpson Model 269, 100,000 ohms-per-volt sensitivity on DC Volts scale.

Courtesy Triplett Electrical Instrument Co.

Fig. 2-15. Triplett Model 630-NS, 200,000 ohms-per-volt sensitivity on DC Volts scale.

other ranges is shown in Fig. 2-15. In this meter, the sensitivity on the AC ranges is also high, being 10,000 ohms per volt for some ranges and 20,000 ohms per volt for others. A new type of movement is employed, it appeared in some commercial instruments in late 1961 or early 1962. This is a suspension movement in which no bearings, jewels, or spiral springs are employed, thus reducing friction. The meter movement is rated at 5 microamperes for a full-scale deflection.

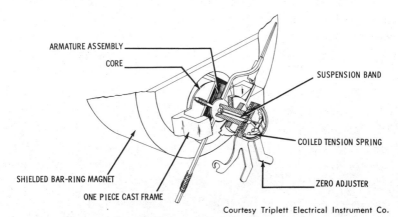

Courtesy Triplett Electrical Instrument Co.

Fig. 2-16. Principle of suspension-band movement.

A meter using this type of *taut-band* suspension is shown in the VOM of Fig. 2-15. The principle of this version of the taut-band suspension movement is shown in Fig. 2-16. The suspension band is a short, very thin, narrow strip of special alloy tightly suspended on special spring terminals. These terminals support the coil and its movable counterparts. The coiled spring terminals protect the band from shock from all directions. When current flows through the meter movement, the pointer is deflected and, being fastened to the suspension band, acts to twist the band slightly. The higher the current is, the greater is the twist. When current ceases, the band tends to untwist, returning the pointer to the zero position.

Other advantages of the meter movement shown in Fig. 2-16 are wide frequency response (the VOM using it is rated at being flat between 20 cps and 100 kc) and its ability to withstand fairly heavy overload, and good accuracy.

Chapter 3

Inside the VOM

Up to this point some of the basic circuits and features of VOM's have been considered. It is now time to examine the physical makeup of the VOM with regard to its components; the types of test leads used; the shunt and multiplier resistors; switches and potentiometers; batteries; fuses; and other components. The purpose here is mainly to get an idea of what the inside of some typical VOM's look like and to be able to identify and locate individual parts.

TEST LEADS, PROBES, AND CLIPS

Ordinarily, one pair of test leads is provided by the manufacturer of a VOM. Leads of about 3 feet long are common, like those in Fig. 3-1. One is covered with red rubber insulation, and the other has black rubber insulation. Fastened to one end of each test lead is a plug for inserting the lead into the VOM jack. Usually the plug on the black test lead is plugged into the jack marked Common, Negative, or Minus. The plug on the red test lead is inserted into the other jack, which may be labelled Ohms, Volts, Amps, Output, etc. At the other end of each test lead is usually either a spring-loaded clip (Fig. 3-1A), with jaws for fastening the clip to the circuit or component being tested, or a test probe (Fig. 3-1B) that is held in the hand and touched to the circuit or component. Sometimes the black test lead is supplied with the clip, and the red lead comes with the test probe. Other special-purpose test leads also are available.

The owner of a VOM may want to obtain additional test leads or replace leads that have become defective. These may be purchased from the VOM manufacturer, from some other manufacturers, a local supplier, or a mail order house. When

ordering, the model number of the instrument should be specified, since not all test leads are interchangeable, especially
with regard to the tips of the plugs inserted in the meter jacks.
It is also practical to assemble your own test leads, using the
proper wire, plugs, and clips or probes.

Test Lead Wire

Standard test lead wire is available from several manufacturers and suppliers. The usual type, as shown in Fig.
3-2A, is about ⅛ inch in diameter. The outer covering is a
rubber insulation; inside the rubber, the stranded wire conductors are spiral-wrapped in a cotton covering for added
strength. The wire usually is No. 18, but in some leads No. 22
wire is used. All, or nearly all, of the strands are copper.
Standard test lead wire is generally rated at either 5,000 to
10,000 working volts. Test leads should be safe and flexible
for easy use, and the conductors should have a low resistance.
Therefore, ordinary wire, even if generally similar in appear-

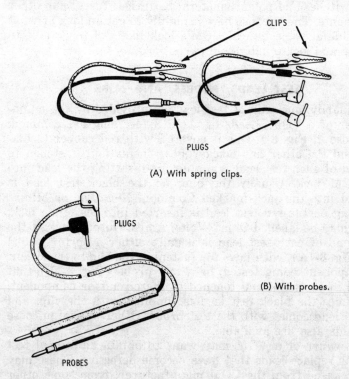

(A) With spring clips.

(B) With probes.

Fig. 3-1. Typical VOM test leads.

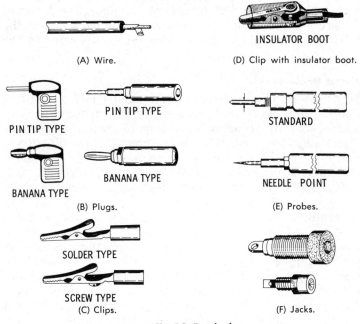

(A) Wire.	INSULATOR BOOT
	(D) Clip with insulator boot.
PIN TIP TYPE PIN TIP TYPE	STANDARD
BANANA TYPE BANANA TYPE	NEEDLE POINT
(B) Plugs.	(E) Probes.
SOLDER TYPE	
SCREW TYPE	
(C) Clips.	(F) Jacks.

Fig. 3-2. Test leads.

ance, is not satisfactory since it usually tends to tangle, kink, or to be too stiff.

Plugs

Test lead plugs are made with several types of conductive tips and in several shapes or configurations (Fig. 3-2B). Typically, the plugs are either of the pin-tip type or the banana-plug type, which is larger in diameter and made of springlike sections for added tension and better contact in the VOM jack. Most manufacturers of higher quality instruments provide the banana plug type.

The body of the plug is generally either a red or black hard rubber or plastic that covers the tip to protect the user from shock. On preassembled test leads, the two halves of the body may be riveted together, but on plugs purchased individually, the two halves are usually fastened together with a machine screw and nut that may be removed for fastening the test lead. In other types of plugs the tip is covered with a barrel-shaped plastic cylinder that may be unscrewed from the tip. On one version of this type of plug, the wire of the test lead must be soldered to the tip terminal; on another, the wire is inserted through the back of the tip, passed through a hole leading out the side of the plug, and fastened by the pressure of a cap nut screwed on the back end of the plug. The most reliable method is to solder the wire to the plug.

Clips and Probes

The probes or clips used at the measuring end of the test leads are also of several different types. The spring type with jaws are generally classified according to shape or assembly as either alligator, crocodile, or meshtooth clips. There are several physical sizes of each of these: heavy duty, standard, or miniature. Some are provided with protective plastic handles (Fig. 3-2) or rubber or plastic protective coverings, (Fig. 3-2D) to avoid shock while handling. Both the solder and screw-terminal methods for fastening are available. Clips also are available; they are constructed so that they can be attached to the end of a probe tip, thus making a single set of test leads quite versatile.

Several types of test probes also are available. The types most frequently used are shown in Fig. 3-2E, and consist of a pointed or thin tip fastened to a protective handle of 4 to 6 inches in length, usually colored red or black. The test lead wire is soldered or fastened by a screw or a pressure nut, depending on the type of probe utilized.

Test leads, probes, plugs, and clips should be inspected regularly for good electrical connection, for loose strands of wire that could cause a shock or a short circuit, and for breaks in the test lead insulation for the same reason. The proper size test-lead plugs should always be used. Never force plugs that are too large into the jacks (examples shown in Fig. 3-2F) of a VOM, or proper contact later might be hard to obtain. Plug tips that are too small should not be used, not only because of the poor contact that might result, but also because the intermittent contact made as the plug tips wobble in the jacks might cause arcing between the tip and the jack. This could result in pitting and perhaps a defective electrical connection, when the proper size plug is later employed.

High-Voltage Test Probe

Many VOM's are designed to measure up to 5,000 to 6,000 volts or more, with the test leads provided. No attempt should ever be made to measure voltage any higher than that for which the meter was designed, unless a high-voltage probe is employed. (Fig. 3-3.) It is better to obtain a high-voltage probe made for your instrument rather than to construct one or adapt one made for another VOM.

The voltage-dropping or multiplier resistor contained in the specially designed handle of a high-voltage probe makes it possible to adapt a VOM for measuring higher voltages. The resistor value is selected by the manufacturer to match the voltmeter ranges and sensitivity. Instructions accompanying the high-voltage probe list the ranges and multiplying factors for interpreting the readings.

The method of operation of a high-voltage test probe is fairly simple. Suppose a particular meter is rated at 20,000 ohms per volt. Then, on the 3-volt range the VOM has a re-

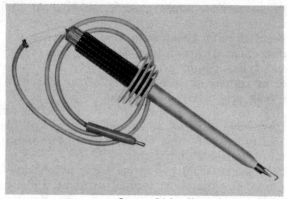

Courtesy Triplett Electrical Instrument Co.

Fig. 3-3. High voltage test probe.

sistance of 60,000 ohms. To measure up to 30,000 volts when the VOM is set to the 3-volt range, a total measuring-circuit resistance of 30,000 × 20,000, or 600 megohms is required. The multiplying resistor in the handle of the probe must then have a value of 600,000,000 − 60,000, or 599,940,000 ohms. In use the common lead of the VOM would be connected to one side of the high voltage source and the tip of the high voltage probe to the other side. With the range switch set to 3 volts, the reading is obtained from the 3-volt scale, multiplying the reading obtained by 30,000/3, or 10,000. However, rather than dealing with the cumbersome multiplier 10,000, the 3-volt range setting of the selector switch could be used, reading from the 300-volt scale and multiplying the reading by 100. The high-voltage probe can be adapted for use at other high-voltage ranges by employing other settings of the range-selector switch, other scales on the meter, or both.

An important feature of a high-voltage probe is that it is designed to protect the user from shock. The flange located near the upper end of the handle (Fig. 3-3) is to prevent the user from placing his hand too close to the high-voltage end of the voltage-dropping resistor or too close to the high-voltage circuit being measured. The dropping resistor is made physically long (or consists of several resistors in series) to distribute the voltage gradient over a path as long as possible. This long path helps to prevent arcing in the resistor and reduces the danger of shock to the user.

RESISTORS USED IN VOM's

The typical resistor types used in VOM's for multipliers and shunts often have at least 1 percent accuracy. According to the manufacturing techniques employed, they are known as deposited carbon, carbon film, deposited film, fixed film, or wire-wound types. Shunt resistors of very low value consist of a piece of copper or iron wire or strap whose resistance has been very accurately determined.

Of course, should a resistor in a VOM become damaged, as from excessive current, it should be replaced by one of the identical type, preferably obtained from the manufacturer or the manufacturer's distributor.

Practically every VOM has at least one potentiometer, that one being used for the ohms zero-adjustment. Potentiometers used in VOM's are usually of the carbon type. Some examples of the types of potentiometers found in measuring instruments are shown in Fig. 3-4. The example in Fig. 3-4A has a shaft sufficiently long to extend through the instrument panel; the shaft is designed so that a knob may be fastened to the end. The one shown in Fig. 3-4B has a knurled shaft for turning with the fingers; in addition, a slot in the end of the shaft is for screwdriver adjustment. The potentiometer shown in Fig. 3-4C is a printed circuit type, which mounts to the board by means of the tabs on each side and is screwdriver adjusted. In Fig. 3-4D is shown a wire-wound potentiometer; this type is usually not employed in a VOM, especially in the voltage measuring circuits, because of its inductance which affects the higher frequency measurements.

SWITCHES

Practically every VOM employs at least one rotary selector switch for changing from one range of voltage, current, or

(A) Shaft for knob.

(B) Knurled and slotted shaft.

(C) Printed circuit type.

(D) Wire wound type.

Fig. 3-4. Potentiometers.

resistance to another. These switches consist of one to four or more wafers, with one or two decks of switch contacts per wafer, and two to twelve or more contacts per deck. An example of one type of rotary selector switch is shown in Fig. 3-5A.

Sometimes slide switches, similar to the one in Fig. 3-5B are employed in VOM's. These are single-pole, single-throw (SPST), single-pole, double-throw (SPDT), double-pole, single-throw (DPST), or double-pole, double-throw (DPDT). Toggle switches (Fig. 3-5C), also are employed with SPST, SPDT, DPST, or DPDT contacts.

TYPICAL VOM's, INTERNAL CONSTRUCTION

An internal view of a typical VOM, the Triplett 630, showing examples of the use of some of the components previously discussed, is shown in Fig. 3-6. A front view of this VOM was shown earlier (Fig. 2-2). The schematic is also shown

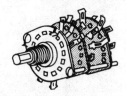

Fig. 3-5. Switches used in VOM's.

here (Fig. 3-7), not so much for analyzing the circuit of the instrument but more to compare the physical appearance of the parts with their location and function in the instrument.

The battery that is visible in the photograph is a 1.5-volt ordinary flashlight type battery, designated B2 in the diagram. Located below B2, but not visible in the photo, is B1—a 30-volt battery used for the higher resistance ranges. A 1-ampere fuse F1 is connected in series with the Common jack; a spare fuse is provided, shown in the lower right of the photo. The fuse protects the metering circuits from the accidental application of excessive currents.

The ohms-zero potentiometer, R32, is a 5 percent carbon, adjustable resistor. All other resistors in the VOM are 1 percent carbon film resistors, except R5, R7, and R15, which are 1 percent wire-wound type. R5 and R7 are in the ohms circuit, and R15 is the 120-milliampere current shunt. Other ohms-circuit resistors include R32, R6, R8, R9, and R10. Other current shunts include R11, R12, R13, and R14.

The rectifier assembly is shown located in the center of the circle formed by the resistors and other parts. The DC voltage dropping resistors include R18, R19, R20, R21, R22, R23, and

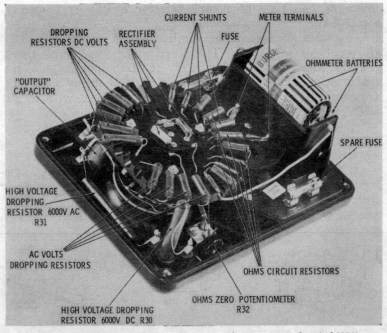

Fig. 3-6. Internal view showing construction and components of typical VOM.

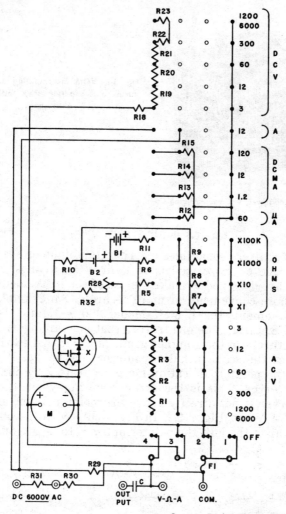

Courtesy Triplett Electrical Instrument Co.

Fig. 3-7. Schematic of VOM of Fig. 2-2 and Fig. 3-7.

the high-voltage dropping resistor for the 6,000 volt DC range, R31.

The AC voltmeter range resistors consist of R1, R2, R3, R4 and the high-voltage dropping resistor for the 6,000 volt AC range, R30.

The actual rotary selector-switch is not visible in Fig. 3-6, but in Fig. 3-7 this switch is represented by the four vertical rows of contacts; the switch is shown in the Off position in this diagram. The arm contacts are represented by the arrowheads.

Fig. 3-8. VOM incorporating anti-parallax mirror and separate scale indication for each range.

Courtesy B & K Manufacturing Co.

RANGE-INDICATING VOM's

Manufacturers sometimes incorporate unique or special features in one or more models of their VOM's; most of these features are designed to make the use of the instrument faster, easier, more convenient, or more accurate. An example of one such instrument, the B & K Model 360 VOMatic, is shown in Fig. 3-8. First, note one feature that is available from most manufacturers in their higher grade models; that is, the lower portion of the scale includes a mirror that makes it possible to read the pointer indication more accurately by eliminating parallax error. This is the error resulting when the eye of the observer is not directly above the meter pointer, as shown in Fig. 3-9A and Fig. 3-9C. In Fig. 3-9A, with the observer's eye too far to the left, the pointer appears to be at 150.5 volts;

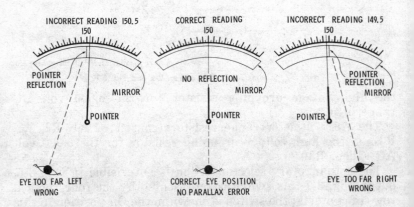

Fig. 3-9. Use of mirrored scale to avoid parallax error.

46

Fig. 3-10. Scale cylinder and gearing arrangement for VOM of Fig. 3-8.

Courtesy B & K Manufacturing Co.

in Fig. 3-9C, with the observers eye too far to the right, the pointer appears to be at 149.5 volts. However, in Fig. 3-9B, the observer knows that his eye is directly above the pointer since the pointer and its mirror image coincide, and the correct reading in this instance of 150 volts is observed.

Perhaps the major different feature, however, included in the VOM of Fig. 3-8 is that the reading of the meter scales is made particularly convenient by the fact that in the scale window only the scale in use is visible. Also, the scale calibration figures are read directly—no multiplying factors are involved. The range selector switch is gear-coupled to a cylinder so that as the range is changed, the cylinder on which the scales are printed rotates, and the next proper scale associated with that range comes into view. Thus, the possibility of reading the wrong scale or of using the wrong multiplying factor is eliminated. An internal rear view of the scale drum or cylinder, and the gearing arrangement is shown in Fig. 3-10.

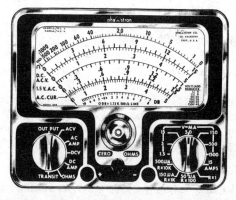

Fig. 3-11. VOM providing AC current measurement.

Plastic sheets on which are printed other supplemental scales are also provided with the VOM of Figs. 3-8 and 3-10. These scales can be cut from the plastic sheets and inserted in the dial window. The supplemental scales include those for measurement of capacitance, millivolts, decibels, audio power in watts, and so on.

Another instrument, the Phaostron 555A VOM (Fig. 3-11), is of interest in that it includes an AC current measuring facility. Protection of the meter movement by means of a diode circuit is shown in Fig. 3-12. Although some VOM's do include diode-rectifier meter-protection circuits, very few provide for AC current measurement. Meter-protecting diode X2 is shown connected across the meter in the schematic, Fig. 3-12. Like other 20,000 ohms-per-volt VOM's, this instrument employs a 50-microampere movement that is deflected full scale by 250 millivolts. The diode type is such that, with its cathode connected to the plus terminal of the meter and its anode to the minus terminal, it will not conduct voltages up to slightly above 250 millivolts. At some voltage slightly above 250 millivolts, however, the diode breaks down or conducts reverse current, thus bypassing this excessive current around the meter, protecting it from damage.

VOM ACCESSORIES

Sometimes accessory items may be included with a VOM when purchased, or accessories may be obtained separately from the manufacturer. Various types of accessories are available; some make it easier to use the instrument, to make measurements more accurately or more conveniently; others extend the range of the instrument. Some examples of these will be considered briefly.

External High-Current Shunts

For most of the VOM's discussed in this book, external shunts are available for extending the range upward for DC current measurement. The shunt usually plugs into the front-panel jacks of the VOM and is calibrated for the specific VOM to extend a certain range to, say, 30 amperes, 60 amperes, or 120 amperes. External shunts should be obtained from the manufacturer for the exact model of instrument employed.

Carrying Cases and Stands

For most VOM's, carrying cases are available; usually these are leather but some are hard plastic. A carrying case is a

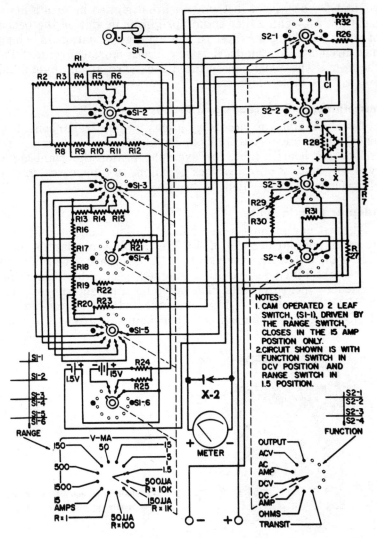

Fig. 3-12. Schematic of VOM shown in Fig. 3-11.

good investment for several reasons. Its main function is to provide portability. A carrying case also is a protection for a delicate instrument—from physical shock, moisture, dust and dirt, and from objects that might accidently strike or fall on the VOM.

Also available are metal, wire, rubber, or plastic stands that are designed so that the VOM may be placed at an angle convenient for use. Most instruments are designed in such a manner that, they can either stand upright or lie flat on the bench or other working surface. In the average situation in which measurements are made, it is sometimes more convenient for the user if the VOM can be tilted backward at an angle from 30 degrees to 60 degrees.

Miscellaneous Test Leads and Probes

Also available as accessory items are miscellaneous test leads and probes. A technician having straight plugs at the end of his leads might, for example, prefer the right-angle type. Or, instead of test probes he might, in some cases, prefer alligator clips, or needlepoint probes.

Adaptor Plug-In Units

At least one manufacturer makes plug-in adaptor units for its most popular models of VOM's. A plug-in adaptor unit, Fig. 3-13, plugs into the front of the standard VOM, shown above it, and includes facilities designed specifically for making particular measurements. The adaptor unit shown converts the VOM to an audio wattmeter for the installation and service of high-fidelity systems and other audio systems, for tele-

Fig. 3-13. Simpson Model 260 VOM with audio-wattmeter plug-in adaptor unit.

Courtesy Simpson Electric Co.

phone, intercoms and public address systems. By means of the switch at the center, the desired load impedance, 4, 8, 16, or 600 ohms, may be selected. In the direct position of this switch, normal use of the VOM is restored without removal of the adaptor.

Other adaptors available for use with this manufacturer's VOM's include the following: transistor tester, temperature tester, AC ammeter, microvolt attenuator, battery tester, milli-ohmeter, and extended-range DC ammeter. The main advantage of an adaptor unit (over purchase of a special measuring instrument) is that some savings are obtained since the adaptor does not include a meter movement of its own, utilizing instead the one in the VOM.

Chapter 4

Putting the VOM to Work

The specifications for a VOM describe the functions and limitations of the VOM. Knowing the "specs" for your VOM, or one you are about to purchase, is very important in using it effectively.

SPECIFICATIONS AND THEIR MEANING

Some of the specifications and terms important to know include sensitivity, accuracy, and frequency response.

Sensitivity

Sensitivity has previously been discussed to a considerable extent. This specification indicates how many volts, millivolts, milliamperes, or microamperes are required for full-scale deflection of the meter. It has been shown that a meter having a movement rated at 1,000 ohms per volt has 1 milliampere flowing through the movement when the pointer is deflected full scale. Also, a 20,000 ohms-per-volt instrument is deflected full scale when 250 millivolts are applied to the movement terminals—at full scale, 50 microamperes are flowing through the movement. The 20,000 ohms-per-volt VOM is the most widely used for general electronics servicing work, but there are available other instruments having 100,000 ohms-per-volt and 200,000 ohms-per-volt sensitivity ratings.

The sensitivity rating attributed to a VOM generally refers to its performance for measuring DC volts. For measuring AC volts, the sensitivity generally is lower for most VOM's. For most better quality VOM's, the AC sensitivity is 5,000 ohms per volt, sometimes 2,000 ohms per volt; or, even 1,000 or 10,000 ohms per volt, depending on the nature and the design of the rectifier circuit. For the lower AC ranges, sometimes a high AC sensitivity is quite useful, for example, when measuring a low-level input signal to an amplifier stage across a high-value grid resistor.

Insertion Loss

The term "insertion loss" sometimes applied to a VOM describes its sensitivity or loading effect when used for measuring current. For examples, the insertion loss for a 20,000 ohms-per-volt VOM when used for measuring direct current usually is specified as 250 millivolts. This 250 millivolts is called a loss because when the meter is in the circuit, it reduces the voltage applied to the circuit being measured by 250 millivolts when the current deflects the pointer full scale.

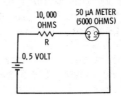

Fig. 4-1. Insertion loss due to presence of current-measuring meter.

If the circuit voltage is fairly high compared to 250 millivolts, this loss is negligible. However, if the applied voltage is fairly close in value to 250 millivolts, and this applied voltage is fixed, the current reading obtained will not be a true indication of the amount of current in the circuit under normal conditions. For example, in Fig. 4-1 the applied voltage is 0.5 volts, or 500 millivolts and the value of R is 10,000 ohms. By Ohm's law, the current is $0.5 \div 10,000 = 0.00005$ ampere, or 50 microamperes. For a 20,000 ohms-per-volt meter movement, there will be no shunt when the switch is set for the 50-microampere range, so the resistance contributed to the circuit by the meter will be 250 millivolts/50 microamperes or 5,000 ohms. This 5,000 ohms in series with the 10,000 ohms of R brings the circuit resistance to 15,000 ohms. And, under this condition, the current now flowing in the circuit and indicated by the meter will be $0.5 \div 15,000$, or 33 microamperes. The voltage applied to R (the voltage drop across it) will be $0.000033 \times 10,000$, or 0.33 volt. The loss contributed by the meter will be $0.000033 \times 5,000$, or 0.17 volt, approximately. Thus, in this case, the insertion loss is 170 millivolts. It is only when the circuit conditions are such that the pointer is deflected full scale when the meter is in the circuit that the insertion loss will be the full 250 millivolts specified.

Accuracy of VOM for Voltage and Current Measurements

The accuracy for most VOM's is between 2 and 5 percent for DC voltages, and 2 and 10 percent for AC voltages. It might be important in some cases to keep in mind exactly how this accuracy factor can affect a reading. Assume that you are using a VOM whose accuracy is given as ±3 percent on the DC voltage ranges. This 3 percent *does not* mean that *any* DC reading obtained will be accurate to within 3 percent. What is *does* mean is that the reading obtained will be accurate within plus or minus 3 percent of the maximum value of the range employed.

Suppose, for example, the 3-volt DC range is used. Then, the reading obtained might be higher or lower than its true value by the amount of 3 percent of 3 volts or, 0.03 × 3 = 0.09 volt. Thus, if the pointer indicates 2.5 volts, the actual voltage might be either 2.5 − 0.09 = 2.41 volts, or 2.5 + 0.09 = 2.59 volts. Similarly, an actual voltage of 2.0 volts might result in a reading anywhere between 2.09 and 1.81 volts, a possible error of 4.5 percent. An actual voltage of 0.5 volt might result in a meter reading between 0.59 volt and 0.41 volt, a possible error of 18 percent.

Thus, on any particular range, the most accurate readings are obtained when the pointer is being deflected as near full scale as possible, and the chance for an erroneous reading increases rapidly for readings of lesser and lesser deflection of the movement.

A general rule of thumb is that voltage and current readings should be taken in the upper ⅔ of the scale. Then, measuring a voltage somewhere in the vicinity of, for example, 0.4 volt, the 0 to 0.5-volt range rather than the 0 to 1-volt or the 0 to 3-volt range should be used.

For the usual good-quality VOM, typical accuracies are ±3 percent for DC ranges, ±5 percent for AC ranges, and ±3 percent for current ranges.

Accuracy of VOM for Resistance Measurement

A VOM whose accuracy is given as 3 percent for the DC voltage ranges will have the same *basic* accuracy for the measurement of resistance. However, the accuracy for resistance measurement must be specified differently; the reason is that at maximum deflection on the resistance scale the pointer indicates zero ohms, and at minimum deflection the pointer indicates infinity. For this reason the specification usually is given as being within so many degrees of pointer position, or within so many percent of the length of the deflection arc.

On many VOM's the full arc of deflection between maximum and minimum scale values is 100 degrees. Therefore, on these VOM's if the DC voltage accuracy is ±3 percent, the accuracy on the Ohms scales is given as ±3 degrees, or as ±3 percent of the arc length. To determine from a particular resistance reading what the exact resistance might be (the extreme values it might lie between) is not so simple as for determining what the actual voltage might be for a particular reading. However, this is usually a minor matter so long as another general rule of thumb is followed. For resistance measurement, since the resistance scale is crowded toward the high-value end as in Fig. 4-2, resistance readings should be made in the

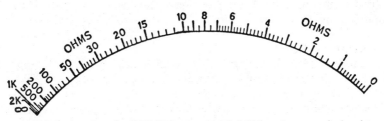

Fig. 4-2. Resistance scale of VOM showing crowded high resistance end of scale.

lower value half of the scale, the higher (toward zero ohms) on the scale, the greater the accuracy. By staying above the half-way deflection point, it is assured that the readings obtained will be accurate to within 6 percent for a ±3 percent scale-length specification. Since it is seldom necessary to measure resistance having a tolerance of less than 5 percent (most are 10 or 20 percent) staying within the upper half of the resistance scale will give fairly reliable results.

Interpreting Ohmmeter Scales

As mentioned earlier, the maximum deflection on a VOM ohmmeter scale is 0 ohms and the minimum deflection is equivalent to infinity. The scale of an ohmmeter is labeled progressively from right to left between 0 and some maximum value at which the scale effectively ends. Assume that the ohms scale of a VOM is calibrated or labeled for values between 0 ohms and 1,000 ohms (1K). In other words, the scale ends at 1K. If the resistance ranges provided were R × 1, R × 100, and R × 100K, the manufacturer of the VOM could say that the VOM has resistance ranges of 0 to 1,000 ohms, 0 to 100,000 ohms, and 0 to 100,000,000 ohms.

For measuring the value of a particular resistor, choice of the proper range to use should be determined from looking at the mid-scale values for each of the ranges available. This mid-scale value for each range cannot be determined from the ranges specified for a VOM. One manufacturer might label his R × 1 range to end at 1K, while another might label his to end at 100K, which would be only a very small distance higher on the scale. The mid-scale value can be determined of course by looking at the ohms scale, but most manufacturers of quality VOM's list the mid-scale values for each range, as well as the end-scale values. Therefore, when considering the purchase of a VOM, the mid-scale values given for each range probably will deserve more serious consideration than the end-scale values. A VOM that has a mid-scale figure of 400 ohms is not as useful for measuring low resistance values as one that is 10 ohms at mid-scale.

Frequency Response

Some VOM's are designed to be accurate on the AC ranges at 60 cycles per second (cps) and in practice do not give a reliable indication at frequencies much above or below 60 cps. Most of the best VOM's of the type previously considered are designed for a consistent response throughout the audio range. Manufacturers differ in the way they specify the response of their instruments. The statement "flat from 50 cps to 50 kc" is a little indefinite. It might mean flat within ½ db, within 1 db, or within 3 db. However, even if the accuracy were within 3 db, it could be assumed that this would be a fairly accurate instrument for measurements over the given range.

A method of specifying the response of a VOM a little more exactly would be as follows, "±½ db, 50 cps to 50 kc, reference 1,000 cps." This means that the VOM is accurate within ±½ db at any frequency between 50 cps and 50 kc as compared to its reading at 1,000 cps.

Some manufacturers include a frequency response chart with their VOM instruction manual. Such a chart, shown in Fig. 4-3 for the VOMatic 360, gives the response for three different AC ranges, the 3-volt, the 15-volt, and the 60-volt ranges. It may be seen that for the 3-volt AC range, there is no variation out to nearly 20 kc; then the response drops off gradually as the frequency is increased, but it is still down only 3 db at a little less than 400 kc. The 3-db response point for the 15-volt range is near 200 kc; for the 60-volt range, the response or deflection *increases* as the frequency is increased.

If this information is not shown in the VOM operation manual, preparing a chart such as this one for any VOM in use will probably be well worth the time and effort involved.

OTHER VOM SPECS

Many other specifications are applied to VOM's and other instruments for electrical measurement, especially laboratory instruments. A detailed discussion of all of these would not

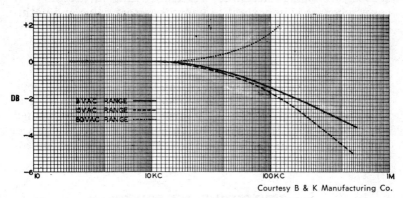

Courtesy B & K Manufacturing Co.

Fig. 4-3. Frequency-response curves of VOMatic 360.

be in line with the main objective of this book. To mention briefly only three; repeatability, tracking, and waveform influence are important.

Repeatability

Repeatability designates a VOM's ability to repeat readings for successive measurements of the same quantity. Some meters will not give exactly the same reading after the test leads are removed and then reapplied to the same test points. This is due mainly to imbalance or friction in the bearings of the movement.

Tracking

Tracking relates to the ability of a meter to indicate accurately over all of its scale. For instance, if a voltage is applied such that exactly full scale deflection results, and then the voltage is reduced to exactly ½ value, the deflection should be exactly 50 percent of full scale similarly, if the voltage is reduced to exactly ¼, the deflection should be exactly ¼, and so on.

Waveform Influence

Nearly all AC VOM's are designed for measurement of the rms values of sine waves. However, meters are deflected in proportion to the average value of the sine-wave half-cycles, or the average value of whatever waveform is applied. If the waveform is not a sine wave, the value indicated probably will not represent the rms value of the waveform being measured. In circuits where pulses and distorted waveforms, for instance, are being measured, remember this discrepancy. In cases where it is important to know the exact value and nature of a voltage or current, the oscilloscope should be used.

BEFORE USING THE VOM

Before using a new VOM, or before using a particular model not used before, it should be examined closely, and the instruction manual provided for the instrument thoroughly studied. Familiarity with the scales, the functions of the switches or controls and the limitations and advantages of the instrument, will be extremely helpful.

ZERO-SETTING THE POINTER

One of the first things to check each time you use a VOM is whether or not the pointer is resting exactly on zero. If the pointer does not indicate zero, it can easily be adjusted. First, place the VOM in the position, horizontal, vertical, or at an angle, in which you intend to use it. Next, with a thin-blade screwdriver, adjust clockwise or counterclockwise the "zero-set" screw usually located near the center of the VOM, just below the faceplate (Fig. 4-4). At the same time you are turn-

Fig. 4-4. Method of adjusting pointer to zero.

ing the zero-set screw, gently tap the case of the VOM to avoid any slight friction or binding that prevents the pointer to turn freely. If you do not begin your measurements with the pointer at zero, your results will not be accurate.

DC VOLTAGE MEASUREMENTS

In preparing to make a DC voltage measurement, first be sure that the two test leads are in the proper jacks. Usually, the black test lead should be in the Common or minus (−) jack and, in most VOM's the red test lead should be plugged into the Plus (+) or Volts jack. If there is a switch marked volts-amps-ohms, or AC/DC, be sure that the switch (or switches) is set to volts and DC.

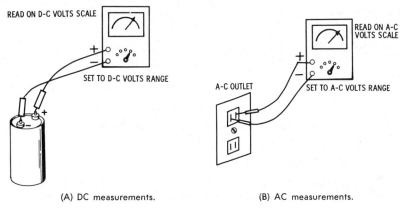

(A) DC measurements.   (B) AC measurements.

Fig. 4-5. DC and AC voltage measurements.

Next, from a schematic or another source, estimate what the voltage to be measured is. Then, with the range switch, select a range that is considerably above this voltage. Turn off the circuit being measured and make sure that no charged capacitors are in the circuit, then connect the test leads across the two points or source of voltage to be measured, as in Fig. 4-5A. Connect the black test lead to the minus side of the circuit and the red test lead to the positive side. Then, standing clear, turn the circuit or equipment on, and note the reading. If the pointer appears to be deflecting backwards, either the polarity of the voltage is opposite to what you had assumed, or you have the test leads reversed in the circuit. You must turn off the equipment, reverse the leads, turn it on again, and once more note the reading. If the pointer does not come

59

to rest in the upper ⅔ of the scale, turn the range switch to the next lower-voltage position; if the pointer is still below the ⅔ point, move the pointer to the next lower setting, and so on. Then, making sure that you are looking at the correct scale for the range you have selected, note the value that the pointer is indicating. For some ranges, the value can be read directly from the scale; for others, it will be necessary to multiply the reading by 10 or 100. For instance, using the 300-volt DC range, and the associated scale is labeled from 0 to 30, and the pointer indicates 25 (Fig. 4-6), you are actually reading 250 volts. Similarly, if the same 0 to 30 scale is used for the 0 to 3 volt range, and a reading of 25 is obtained, the voltage is actually 2.5 volts.

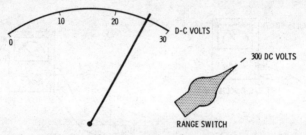

Fig. 4-6. Setting of range switch and position of pointer for 250 volts DC.

In many meters, however, the scales are calibrated for most of the ranges provided; thus multiplying, dividing, or interpreting the readings obtained, as before, is seldom necessary.

Voltage measurements can be made in many cases without turning off the equipment or circuit, if the technician has gained sufficient experience to exercise the proper precautions.

AC VOLTAGE MEASUREMENTS

The procedure for making AC voltage measurements is similar to that for DC voltage. Begin by making sure the pointer is at zero; plug the black lead into the (minus) jack, the red lead into the (plus) or AC jack; set the AC/DC switch (if there is one) to AC and set the range switch to an AC range somewhat higher than the rms value of the estimated voltage to be measured. Check to see that the equipment is turned off. Connect the test leads across the points at which the voltage is to be measured, as in Fig. 4-5B, then turn on the equipment and observe the pointer. If there is no deflection, or only a little deflection, set the range switch to the next lower range, as required, until the pointer is in the upper ⅔ of the scale.

On many VOM's there may be some difference between the calibrated AC scales and the DC scales, so make sure that the correct scale or scales are used for AC. Note in Fig. 4-7 that although the ranges provided for DC measurements are the same as for AC measurements, a different set of scales is provided for each on the meter faceplate. The corresponding calibrations substantially coincide for the high values on both ranges, but for the lower values they do not coincide, as shown by the broken line. Also, as shown, a completely separate scale is provided for the 3-volt AC range. After practice it should be easy to select automatically the proper set of scales for AC or DC measurement.

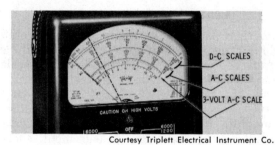

Courtesy Triplett Electrical Instrument Co.

Fig. 4-7. Difference between AC and DC scales at lower values.

DC CURRENT MEASUREMENT

For measuring DC current with a VOM, the circuit in which the current in flowing must be first turned off, and then opened, such as at point X in Fig. 4-8A. The range switch of the VOM should be set to the current range required. The test leads are then connected in series with the break in the circuit, as shown in Fig. 4-8B, and the equipment turned on. The current is read on the DC voltage scale. If the meter indicates somewhat below ⅔ deflection, the range switch should be set to the next lower current range. If a backward reading is obtained, the test leads should be reversed, or, if a polarity switch is provided, it should be turned to the opposite direction. When a VOM is set for measuring current, *NEVER* connect the test leads across a live component or source of voltage; this could burn out the meter movement.

As previously mentioned, most VOM's do not provide for AC current measurement.

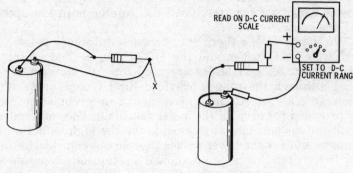

(A) Breaking circuit under test. (B) Insertion of meter in circuit.

Fig. 4-8. Reading current.

MEASUREMENT OF RESISTANCE

To measure resistance, the range switch is rotated to the correct ohms range, depending on the value of the resistance to be measured. For example, if the ohms mid-scale value is 5 ohms, and the estimated value of the resistor being measured is 300 ohms, the range switch should be set to R × 100. If no R × 100 range is provided, the most suitable range is selected to obtain a pointer deflection near mid-scale.

Before making the resistance measurement, short the tips of the test probes or clips together, and adjust the Ohms Zero knob for exactly 0 ohms reading at the extreme right of the scale. Next, connect the test probes across the resistor, as shown in Fig. 4-9. When measuring a resistor in a circuit, at least one end of the resistor should be disconnected from that circuit so that other components in the circuit will not affect the resistance value indicated on the VOM. If it is necessary to change the Ohms range, the pointer should again be set to zero ohms while touching the probe tips together. This calibrates the range in use and assures greater accuracy.

The same scale is used for all resistance readings, with the scale values multiplied by 1, 10, 100, 1,000, 100,000, etc.;

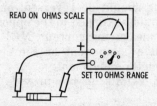

Fig. 4-9. Reading resistance.

these multipliers are determined by the setting of the range switch. On the higher resistance ranges, touching the ends of the resistor or the test-probes with the hands can affect the resistance reading. This is because the body is then connected across the resistor being measured and this parallel resistance lowers the effective value. For high resistance measurements, touching the resistor or probes should be avoided. One method of preventing this in resistance measurements is to use clips rather than probes to connect to the resistor, thus permitting you to be entirely free of the measurement.

OUTPUT MEASUREMENT

The output measurement facility of a VOM is utilized, for example, in measuring the audio output voltage from an amplifier across a speaker, or at the input to an amplifier stage. The output measurement is taken the same as an AC measurement, except that, if an AC/DC/output switch is provided on the VOM, it should be set to Output. This inserts a capacitor in series with one of the test leads, which blocks out any DC present in the circuit that is being measured. The associated AC scale is read for the output value.

Sometimes it is desired to interpret the AC output value obtained in terms of decibels (db). If the VOM includes a db scale, the value in db can be interpreted from that scale. The db value depends on the AC range being used. For example, for the VOM of Fig. 4-7, if the 3-volt AC range is used, read the db value directly from the db scale; when the 12-volt AC range is being used, read the value from the db scale, and add 12 db; if the 60-volt range is being used, read the value from the db scale, and add 26 db; and so on. Note that these instructions are provided in the lower right corner of the meter faceplate. This particular VOM has been calibrated so that the value of 0 db is 1 milliwatt on a 600-ohm line. The db values are therefore only relative if the measurement is not on a 600-ohm circuit. The db values may be converted to a standard reference of 6 milliwatts in a 500-ohm line by subtracting 7 db from the readings obtained by the methods just described.

Chapter 5

Use, Repair and Maintenance

The VOM can be used reliably in practically all general testing, troubleshooting, and maintenance situations, except where unusual accuracy is desired or where unusually high-impedance circuits are being tested. The VOM, itself, rates fairly high in accuracy, but whenever greater accuracy is required, laboratory or precision instruments must be used. For those circuit measurements where the impedance of the circuit is too high for accurate use of the VOM, the VTVM is usually employed; however, as mentioned earlier, some VOM's are available, which exceed the input impedance of the typical VTVM for certain voltage ranges.

APPLICATIONS IN TESTING AND TROUBLESHOOTING

In the first part of this chapter general techniques in applying the VOM and some of the precautions that should be observed will be considered. The remainder of the chapter will be devoted to the care, repair, and maintenance of the VOM.

Measuring Capacitor Leakage Resistance

The VOM can be used to advantage in measuring capacitor leakage resistance. For this test, a high-resistance range is employed, for example, the R ×10,000 range. When the ohmmeter leads are applied to the terminals of an uncharged capacitor, the pointer will deflect in the direction of zero resistance, and then either slowly or quickly (depending on the capacitor) the pointer will come to rest at infinity or at a specific amount of resistance. If the capacitor is open, there will be no deflection of the pointer. If the capacitor is shorted, the pointer will indicate zero ohms and remain there; if the leakage resistance is high, the resistance reading will be fairly high compared to a shorted capacitor.

Generally, the lower the capacitance of the capacitor, the greater will be its measurable resistance in order for it to be considered a good capacitor. Mica and paper capacitors of 0.5 μf to 2.0 μf should measure 20 megohms or more. Lower value capacitors should have an even greater resistance. On the R × 10,000 range, most capacitors that measure infinite ohms probably do not have excessive leakage.

Before the leakage resistance of a capacitor is checked, it is a good idea to discharge the capacitor by shorting the leads

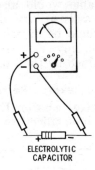

Fig. 5-1. Test lead polarity for measuring electrolytic capacitor leakage.

ELECTROLYTIC
CAPACITOR

together. A charged, high-value capacitor will discharge through the ohmmeter circuit and slam the pointer against the end-stop, damaging the pointer or the movement.

Electrolytic capacitors will indicate a greater leakage (lower resistance) than paper, mica, or oil-filled capacitors. The ohmmeter test leads must be connected across the capacitor terminals in the proper polarity. The red or positive ohmmeter lead should be connected to the positive terminal of an electrolytic capacitor, and the black or common ohmmeter lead should be connected to the negative terminal, as shown in Fig. 5-1. Connection in the reverse manner usually results in a very low resistance reading.

Because low-value capacitors have a leakage resistance that is not measurable on a VOM, the best check on them and on any capacitor, for that matter, is by means of a capacitor tester. In determining the leakage, this instrument applies the rated voltage to the capacitor.

Measurement of Capacitance With VOM

The approximate value of a nonelectrolytic capacitor can be determined with the VOM by measuring its relative reactance at a convenient AC voltage source, such as the power line. The VOM, set on the 300-volt AC range, and the capacitor are connected in series and placed across the 110-volt, 60 cycles-per-second supply as shown in Fig. 5-2. The greater is the AC voltage reading obtained, the larger is the capacitance, assuming that the leakage of the capacitor is low (resistance is high). For a particular VOM a table or graph may be prepared relating the AC voltage reading and capacitance by using several known-good capacitors as standards. Such a table, provided in the instruction manual for the Triplett 630 VOM, is shown in Table 5-1. The AC voltage readings corresponding to various values of capacitance are shown. The same table would also be useful with other similar VOM's having a sensitivity of 5,000 ohms per volt on the AC ranges.

It should be mentioned that this method of measuring capacity is only relatively accurate. A better measurement would be obtained by the use of a capacity checker or an LC bridge.

Forward-Reverse Rectifier Tests

Relative tests on the condition of copper oxide, selenium, germanium, silicon, or other nonvacuum and nongas tube recti-

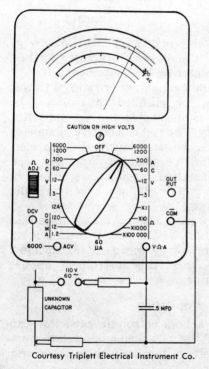

Fig. 5-2. Method of using VOM to measure capacitance.

Courtesy Triplett Electrical Instrument Co.

Table 5-1. Relationship of AC Voltage Readings and Capacitance for Measurement Arrangement Shown in Fig. 5-2

TO MEASURE MFD	SET SELECTOR SWITCH TO	DEFLECTION IN AC VOLTS
0.002		0.45
0.004		0.83
0.006	3 AC volts	1.25
0.008		1.65
0.010		2.10
0.020		4.3
0.04	12 AC volts	7.7
0.05		9.7
0.08		14.5
0.10		17.5
0.2	60 AC volts	30.0
0.4		45.0
0.6		57.0
0.8		65.0
1.0		75.0
2.0	300 AC volts	85.0
5.0		95.0
10.0		100.0

CAUTION: Do not attempt to use this test on electrolytic capacitors.

fiers can be made with the VOM. The measured resistance should be high in one direction and considerably less in the other direction. With the ohmmeter leads connected across the rectifier terminals so that the lesser amount of current flows (reverse direction), the resistance is approximately 10 times greater than it is with the ohmmeter leads connected across the rectifier terminals in the opposite or forward direction.

In using this method of measurement, care should be taken that low-current signal diodes are not damaged from the normal current of the ohmmeter circuit; with some diodes this method should not be used. Since the forward and reverse resistance of a rectifier depend to some extent on the voltage applied across it, the results obtained should be considered only relative. However, in most instances a defective rectifier shows up as being shorted, open, or having a too-low reverse to forward resistance ratio. Fairly positive proof is possible by measuring a similar rectifier known to be good, and comparing the readings obtained to those of the suspected rectifier.

Testing Fused Circuits

One of the most useful applications of the VOM is in testing fuses and fused circuits. The source of trouble can be located quickly and easily with the VOM. The method of testing a fuse is simple. The power should be turned off, the fuse removed from the circuit, and the test leads of the VOM, which is set up as an ohmmeter on the R × 1 range, are connected across the fuse. The resistance should be zero, or at most only a fraction of an ohm, for the average fuse in good condition.

Sometimes a fuse opens or develops a high resistance joint only when the higher current of the circuit in which it is used is flowing through it. In these cases, as when the fuse checks zero ohms by the ohmmeter method, but still no power is available to the equipment when it is turned on, a voltage check should be made. This is done, as shown in Fig. 5-3, by setting up the VOM for a 117-volt AC reading. One of the

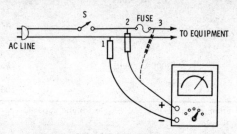

Fig. 5-3. Method for testing fused circuit.

test leads is connected to the unfused side of the line, point 1 (Fig. 5-3). The other test lead is then connected to point 2. The VOM should read the full line voltage if switch S is ON. If the full AC reading is not obtained, the trouble is occurring ahead of the fuse; either in the power switch, the AC line cord, the AC plug, or the AC source. Assuming that the proper AC reading is obtained at point 2 (Fig. 5-3), that test lead is then moved to point 3 (Fig. 5-3). If no AC reading is obtained there (or if the AC reading is substantially low) the fuse is either open or defective.

Locating Open Filaments

The VOM is useful also in locating the open filament in a series-string, vacuum-tube circuit. When one tube filament in a series string opens, current is interrupted in all of the tubes in that string. They all go out, and it is impossible to tell by inspection which tube is defective. One method of locating the open tube is by use of the ohmmeter section of the VOM, measuring across each filament; the filament measuring infinite ohms is the open filament.

Another method is by a voltage check, as shown in Fig. 5-4A. When the VOM, set up as an AC voltmeter, is connected across a good filament, no voltage reading will be indicated.

This is different if the filament circuit is continuous in which case the voltmeter will indicate the voltage across the filament. In an open circuit, no current flows through the filament, and therefore there is no voltage drop across it to deflect the meter. However, when the VOM is connected across the open filament, the full voltage of the source will be indicated on

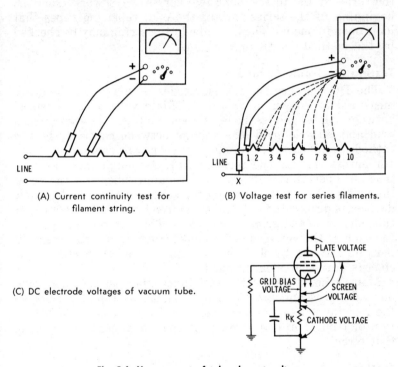

(A) Current continuity test for filament string.

(B) Voltage test for series filaments.

(C) DC electrode voltages of vacuum tube.

PLATE VOLTAGE

GRID BIAS VOLTAGE

SCREEN VOLTAGE

R_K CATHODE VOLTAGE

Fig. 5-4. Measurement of tube element voltages.

the meter. The VOM indicates the full voltage rather than the rated voltage of the filament because the resistance of the VOM is much greater than that of the filament; therefore, the voltage drop across the meter approaches the applied voltage. The connection of the VOM across the open filament completes the circuit, permitting a small amount of current to flow and, thus, to deflect the meter. This is not an effective test if two tubes in the string have open filaments. In such a case there will be no voltage reading on any tube in the series.

A more common and more reliable method is shown in Fig. 5-4B. The meter, set on an AC range that will handle the full line voltage is connected with one lead to the common side of the line at point X, Fig. 5-4B. The other lead is then moved progressively from point 1 through points 2, 3, 4, 5, 6, etc., getting a slightly lower voltage reading at each tube. If a point is reached where zero voltage is indicated, the tube at that point has an open filament. Replace this tube and proceed to the next filament test points—toward the common end of the series string in the same manner. Always work from the beginning of the series toward the end, replacing tubes that have open filaments. The last tube in the string may be checked by the method shown in Fig. 5-4A.

Testing Electronic Circuits

The DC voltages for the electrodes of a vacuum tube are measured as shown in Fig. 5-4C. Plate voltage is measured between plate and cathode, screen voltage between screen grid and cathode, grid bias voltage between control grid and cathode, and cathode voltage between cathode and ground (or across the cathode resistor R_K). Although these are the true DC operating voltages for a vacuum tube, in many cases the voltage lists accompanying the schematic for an electronic device are designated as being measured between the particular tube electrode and ground or chassis. This reference to ground for each of the voltages is for convenience in measurement; it permits leaving the negative or common lead connected to the chassis for each measurement.

Many schematics list the resistance readings between various tube pins and ground. Any serious discrepancy between the resistance listed and the measured resistance is an indication of trouble in one or more of the components common to that circuit.

Testing Batteries

The VOM is useful for testing the condition of batteries. It should always be remembered that it is best to measure the output voltage of a battery when the battery is under load, or actually being used in the equipment. As a battery deteriorates or becomes discharged, its internal resistance increases. The load current flowing through this internal resistance reduces the output voltage appearing across the battery terminals. If the load current is not flowing, as when the battery is tested out of the circuit, the voltage is not reduced by the internal resistance, and the battery may test good. In many cases, badly

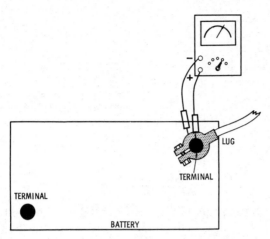

Fig. 5-5. Measuring voltage drop across battery connections.

deteriorated batteries measure low in voltage even when removed from the circuit. Any battery that measures 75 percent or less of rated voltage under load is considered weak and should be either charged or replaced, depending on the type of battery.

The VOM is very useful for checking the operation of automobile batteries. In many cases, a poor connection due to dirt or corrosion develops between a battery terminal and the clamp or lug fastened to it. When a battery measures full output voltage across its terminals, but poor starting, or other electrical troubles are experienced, measure the battery output voltage across the lugs fastened to the battery terminals, and then measure across the terminals themselves. If the voltage measured across both points is not the same, poor electrical contact exists between one terminal and its associated lug. The connection that is involved can be determined by measuring for a voltage difference across the contact points. To do this, place one test lead on the battery terminal and the other lead on the lug connected to the terminal (Fig. 5-5). Any measurable voltage drop is a sufficient reason to remove and clean the connection to correct the difficulty.

Measurements in Sensitive Circuits

In some cases, connecting a VOM to a sensitive, high-gain or sharply-tuned circuit upsets the operation of the circuit being tested so that the reading obtained is not representative of actual operating conditions. Measurement in such circuits is best made with a VTVM which has a higher-resistance

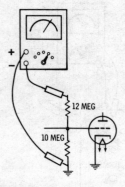

Fig. 5-6. Use of high value resistor in series with test lead for sensitive circuits.

input. If this equipment is not available, the next best approach is to use a resistor in series with the positive test lead of the VOM as shown in Fig. 5-6. The series resistor that is selected should have a value higher than the impedance of the circuit being measured. With the use of the series resistor, the reading will not be as accurate, but often only a relative reading is required.

Where accuracy is important, the reduction due to the series resistor may be calculated. The series resistor and the resistance of the VOM on the scale employed may be considered to be a voltage divider. For example, assume that a voltage is to be measured across a 10 megohm circuit, and the series resistor selected is 12 megohms. If the 300-volt DC range on a 20,000 ohms-per-volt VOM is employed, the meter resistance then is $300 \times 20,000 = 6$ megohms. The voltage divider is then a 12 megohm resistor in series with a 6 megohm resistor, with the measurement occurring across the 6 megohm resistor. With the total resistance 18 megohms, only ⅓ of the voltage is read by the meter; therefore, the reading obtained should be multiplied by 3.

The manufacturer of the RCA WV38A VOM provides the following table in the instruction manual, listing the multiplier and the reading for specific values of series resistance (Table 5-2).

Table 5-2. Readings Obtained Using Series Resistors to Decrease Loading Effect

RANGE	RESISTOR	READING MULTIPLIER	SCALE TO READ
2.5 V	50 K	2 X	5 V
2.5 V	150 K	4 X	10 V
50 V	1 Meg	2 X	100 V
250 V	5 Meg	2 X	500 V

PRECAUTIONS IN USE OF VOM

Caution is essential when working on, or when using the VOM to make measurements on electrical and electronic equipment. You should always be alert to the possibility that the same cause of faulty operation might also cause dangerously high voltage to be present at places least expected.

A good practice is to work with one hand behind you or in your pocket. This is some protection against getting across points of potential difference. Be sure to avoid standing on conductive, damp, or wet surfaces when making measurements; instead, if possible, stand on a dry board. Try to stand

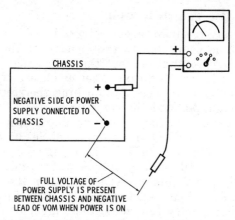

Fig. 5-7. Shock danger of improperly connected VOM.

clear of the equipment, so that other points on your body do not touch the equipment when you are connecting or disconnecting a test lead.

When making resistance measurements, be sure the power is off and that all capacitors that might hold a charge have been discharged by shorting across their terminals with an insulated test lead or a screwdriver having an insulated handle.

Sequence of Test Lead Connection

When connecting the VOM to a circuit for a voltage measurement, the common or negative lead should be connected first to the chassis of the equipment on which the measurement is being made then the positive test lead is connected. Fig. 5-7 illustrates what may happen if this practice is ignored. Note that in Fig. 5-7 the positive or red test lead is connected to the positive voltage point. If you then happen to hold or touch the tip of the negative test probe and, at the same time, with your other hand touch the chassis (to which the negative lead of the meter is to be connected), practically the full voltage existing across the positive and negative points of the equipment under test will be impressed across your body and the meter. The resistance of the body, normally fairly high, in series with the VOM, receives a high percentage of the voltage.

For the reason just mentioned, when test leads are disconnected, the positive, or high potential, lead should be disconnected first, the negative lead, or the one connected to the chassis should be disconnected last.

Determining if a Chassis is "Hot"

"Hot" chassis receivers are receivers in which one side of the AC input is connected to the chassis. If the set is connected to the AC output so that the ungrounded side of the AC power line is the one to the receiver chassis, it is possible to receive a dangerous shock by touching the receiver chassis and some ground point at the same time.

The VOM can be employed to determine whether or not the receiver chassis is hot relative to ground. Set up the VOM to measure 117 volts AC, as shown in Fig. 5-8. Connect one test lead to a ground point such as a water pipe, radiator, or electric stove frame, and connect the other test lead to the receiver chassis. If the VOM reads the full line voltage, or even more than a very few volts, the danger of shock exists. To correct this condition, remove the AC power plug from the wall outlet, rotate it 180 degrees, and reinsert it in the wall outlet. Again use the VOM to measure between chassis and

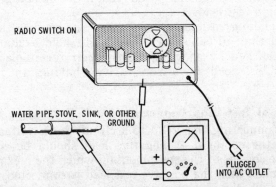

RADIO SWITCH ON

WATER PIPE, STOVE, SINK, OR OTHER GROUND

+

−

PLUGGED INTO AC OUTLET

Fig. 5-8. Using VOM to check "hot chassis" equipment for shock hazard.

ground. There should now be no measurable voltage, and the receiver is safer to work on.

Test Lead Inspection

Test leads should be inspected regularly for broken or frayed leads that could present a shock hazard to the user. Replace or repair such test leads immediately. After a VOM test is completed, it should be disconnected from the circuit at once; otherwise you or some other person might unknowingly pick up the VOM and test leads and either receive a bad shock, or cause a short in the equipment to which the leads are connected.

It is good practice, when working on equipment in which more than 40 to 50 volts exist, to have someone nearby in the event you do receive a serious shock.

Finally, *never* make measurements with a VOM that has been removed from its cabinet.

CARE AND MAINTENANCE

Manufacturers make VOM's as rugged as possible for a delicate instrument, but there is a limit to the abuse an instrument of high sensitivity can withstand.

Care In Selecting Range

It was mentioned earlier, but it is worth repeating, that for current and voltage measurements always begin with a range higher than the voltage or current expected. This will provide some assurance that the meter will be protected if the voltage or current is excessive. Double-check before connecting the test leads. If the range switch is accidently left in the Ohms positions, or on a low range, one or more components, or the meter movement (a pretty expensive item) may be destroyed.

Protection from Physical Damage

Always store the VOM where it will not fall or accidently be knocked down; even if the meter cabinet does not break, the pivot of the pointer may be jarred from its bearings. Replacing or repairing any part of the meter movement is usually a job for a specially trained technician. It is usually necessary to return the instrument to the factory for repair and recalibration. Never place the VOM on a workbench where power tools are used or where excessive vibration is present. Avoid having the VOM where metal chips or metallic dust is present;

if these get inside the case of the instrument, a short or other trouble may develop. Do not place the VOM where excessively high or low temperatures are likely to occur or where excessive moisture or dampness may cause leakage between components, wire, or switch contacts, or cause deterioration of the batteries.

REMOVAL OF VOM FROM CASE

On some occasions it is necessary to remove the VOM from the case—at least to change the batteries. These get weak after long usage. The first and most obvious sign of aging batteries is that it becomes impossible to bring the pointer to zero in the resistance range, with the test leads shorted together. There is usually some movement of the pointer, even with weak batteries.

For the lower resistance ranges, usually one or two 1.5-volt dry cells are active in the circuit. For the higher resistance ranges, such as R × 10,000, or R × 100,000, higher voltage (but usually not larger physically) batteries, 4.5-volts, 7.5-volts, 33 volts, 67.5-volts, etc. are sometimes utilized. Therefore, it is possible that the VOM may zero on one or two of the ranges but not on the others. This evidence will show which battery or batteries to replace.

To remove the VOM from its case, it is generally necessary only to remove two to five screws from the back or bottom of the case. These may be either slotted-head screws or Phillips-head screws. After the screws are removed, merely lift the case from the instrument, as shown in Fig. 5-9. If the back

Fig. 5-9. Removal of VOM from case.

of the case does not come free easily, do not try to shake it free without holding the other part of the case with your other hand.

The batteries usually are held in place by a spring type holder, and they should not be difficult to remove. All that is usually necessary is to lift them out of the holder and slide in the new battery. Before putting in the new battery or batteries, look at the metal contacts to see if rust or corrosion has started to appear; if so, clean or scrape the contacts. Try to keep the particles from falling into the instrument—if necessary, use a vacuum to remove them.

Batteries should be replaced with similar types. However, for some batteries there are long-life, industrial, or instrument versions for replacement that might give longer satisfactory performance than the type provided with your VOM. The leakproof type battery should be used, which will help prevent the battery chemicals from damaging delicate or precision components. Batteries should be inserted with proper regard to polarity; the battery holders are almost always marked, one side + and the other −, to correspond to the terminals of the battery.

Fuse Replacement

Should the fuse blow in the VOM, it should be replaced only by an identical fuse. If the fuse is one with a conventional element, it should never be replaced by a slow-blow type of fuse, for this reduces the margin of protection to the meter movement. A fuse in a typical VOM will be a 1-ampere, 250-volt, 3AG type; fuses of other ratings may also be encountered in some meters.

If the VOM fails to respond on all functions, it is possible that either the fuse is open, one of the test leads is open, or there is a break in the wiring to one of the jacks. The meter movement may be defective if there is no response on any function.

Testing the Meter Movement

If it is suspected that the meter movement is defective, do not attempt to repair it yourself; this almost always leads to even more serious damage to the movement. Instead, follow the manufacturer's direction in the VOM instruction manual, and return it to him. Some manufacturers request that you write first, to obtain a "return authorization." Whatever the instructions, follow them closely in order to prevent the meter from becoming lost.

77

Do not attempt to measure the resistance of a meter movement with another VOM, since this will probably cause excessive current to flow through the meter movement.

One way to check the meter movement, if care is used, is as follows: Determine the full-scale current rating of the movement. Remove any connections to the terminals on the back of the movement case. Wire up a circuit consisting of a 1.5-volt battery and series resistor for connection to the meter terminals. Calculate the value necessary for the series resistor to provide about ⅔ full-scale deflection. For example, if the movement is a 50-microampere, 250-millivolt type, the resistor required for full scale will be: $R = \frac{.25}{50} \times 10^6$, or 5,000 ohms. If this value is increased by about 30 percent, to about 6,500

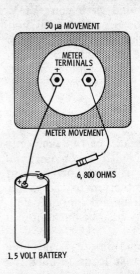

Fig. 5-10. Method for testing meter movement.

ohms, about ⅔ deflection on the meter will be obtained. The circuit for testing the meter as described is shown in Fig. 5-10. A standard 6,800-ohm resistor is shown in the figure. If no deflection is obtained, or it is substantially different from ⅔ of full scale, the movement is probably defective.

Rectifier Replacement

Should the meter fail to work properly on the AC ranges, it is likely the rectifier is defective. An exact replacement rectifier should be used. If two rectifiers are used in the VOM, both should be replaced, using a properly matched set obtained from the manufacturer or authorized distributor. Substitution of a rectifier that is almost, but not quite, the same results in inaccuracy on the AC ranges.

Resistor Replacement

If you have the misfortune to try to measure voltage when your VOM is set to measure ohms, it is possible that one of the resistors in the ohmmeter circuit will open and will have to be replaced. Be sure to replace the resistor with an identical

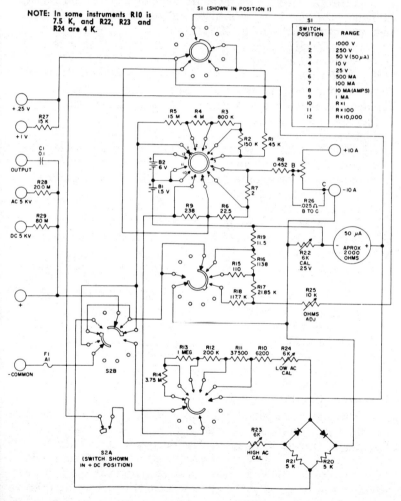

Courtesy Radio Corporation of America

Fig. 5-11. Schematic of RCA WV-38A.

type. If the identical replacement is not available, and the VOM must be used before one can be obtained from the manufacturer, a resistor of identical characteristics—the same value, tolerance, wattage, and composition, can be used.

Calibration of VOM

The accuracy of a VOM can be checked to a sufficient approximation by measuring a known-good battery. New, dry cells should measure about 1.55 volts per cell. The resistance ranges can be checked by measurement of a precision resistor known to be good. VOM's also can be compared with other instruments known to be accurate.

In some VOM's little can be done, other than change parts, if it is discovered that the accuracy is off. Other VOM's include calibration adjustments for this purpose. Ordinarily these should not be touched. However, if components are replaced, especially the rectifier, it is sometimes necessary to adjust these calibration controls.

The circuit of the RCA WV-38A VOM, which includes calibration controls, is shown in Fig. 5-11. According to the manufacturer, these controls may require adjustment if the rectifier is replaced. The procedure suggested by RCA for recalibrating the AC ranges is as follows:

1. Set the AC DC Switch to the AC position.
2. Set the Range Switch to the 250 volt position.
3. Connect the test leads to a known AC voltage source of 250 volts AC.
4. Adjust variable resistor R23 until the meter indicates full scale.
5. Remove the test leads from the 250-volts AC source.
6. Set the Range Switch to the 2.5 volts position.
7. Connect the test leads to a known AC voltage source of 2.5 volts AC.
8. Adjust R24 until the meter indicates full scale.
9. Remove the test leads from the 2.5 volts AC source.

Soldering Connections in VOM

In replacing components or resoldering connections, be sure not to overheat nearby parts; this may change their value. Use a thin-tipped 25 to 40 watt soldering iron. It is important also to use only resin-core solder; never use acid-core solder.

Some VOM's now in use employ printed circuit boards. Always follow closely the direction of the manufacturer in removing and replacing the board for repairs, and when soldering or unsoldering connections or components.

Chapter 6

The VTVM; How It Works

An important part of the operating principle of the vacuum-tube voltmeter (VTVM) is the same as that of the VOM. Current flowing through a D'Arsonval meter movement causes a pointer deflection proportional to the intensity of the current.

VTVM's are also much like VOM's in appearance. Examples are shown in Figs. 6-1 and 6-2. The unit in Fig. 6-1 might be typical of inexpensive, but reliable VTVM's of good performance. The one in Fig. 6-2 is representative of VTVM's designed for maximum versatility and usefulness, and is somewhat more costly. These two represent the two extremes of VTVM's that the average user employs for measurements in servicing and troubleshooting.

In addition to commercially built VTVM's, there are kit types that the purchaser can build from parts provided by

Fig. 6-1. Arkay Model VT-10 VTVM.

Courtesy Arkay International

the manufacturer. An example is shown in Fig. 6-3. Assembling a kit can save the purchaser a good percentage of the cost of a VTVM, if he has the time to assemble it. Assuming that the directions are followed carefully for assembly and calibration, and good soldering practices are employed, a kit VTVM can approach the best commercial models in performance.

Courtesy Radio Corporation of America

Fig. 6-2. RCA WV-87B Master VoltOhmyst.

Courtesy Heath Company

Fig. 6-3. Heathkit Model IM-13 VTVM.

ADVANTAGES AND DISADVANTAGES OF THE VTVM

The major difference between the VOM and the VTVM is that in the VTVM one or more vacuum tubes are employed in the circuit. This has the following advantages, as compared with the VOM:

1. Higher input resistance.
2. Lower input capacitance.
3. Greater sensitivity.
4. Less sensitive, lower-cost meter movement is used.

The higher input resistance permits measurement in circuits having high impedance or resistance with less loading effect than with the typical VOM. The lower input capacitance of the VTVM makes possible measurement of AC voltage at higher frequency than is possible with the VOM. The greater sensitivity of the VTVM, provided by one or more stages of amplification, makes possible the measurement of lower values of voltage and higher values of resistance. The use of the less-sensitive, lower-cost, meter movement is made possible by the amplification provided in the VTVM circuit.

These advantages are of sufficient importance, in many cases, to overlook some disadvantages of the VTVM which are:

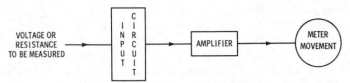

Fig. 6-4. Block diagram of VTVM circuit.

1. The VTVM is less stable than the VOM; The VTVM requires a warm-up time for its greatest accuracy.
2. It must be calibrated more frequently.
3. An external source of power is usually required.
4. The more complex circuitry is subject to more frequent trouble.

The reason for some of these advantages and disadvantages will become apparent later when the basic and typical circuits of VTVM's are discussed.

VTVM PRINCIPLE

Basically, the VTVM consists of an input circuit, an amplifier, and a meter movement, as shown in Fig. 6-4. It is because a vacuum-tube amplifier has a high input resistance, that a VTVM causes less loading when it is connected to a circuit for voltage measurement. The input resistance for typical VTVM's is 10 or 11 megohms or more, on most of the voltage ranges.

Simple VTVM

The simplest type of VTVM for measuring DC voltages is shown in Fig. 6-5. The 1-megohm resistor built into the probe is mainly responsible for minimizing the VTVM input capacitance, or capacitive loading effect. It serves to isolate the VTVM circuits from the circuit being measured. The input resistance of this VTVM circuit consists of the 1-megohm

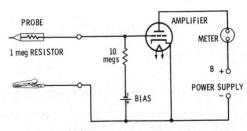

Fig. 6-5. Schematic of basic VTVM circuit.

probe resistor and the 10 megohm grid resistor, a total of 11 megohms. The battery provides a bias for the triode amplifier tube, keeping it at cutoff until the test leads are placed across a positive or an AC source of voltage.

If the voltage being measured is DC, the positive voltage contacted by the probe lowers the bias on the amplifier grid and causes current to flow through the tube and meter movement in proportion to the amplitude of the positive voltage.

If the voltage being measured is AC, the negative half-cycles of the AC voltage have no effect on the amplifier and meter current, since the amplifier is biased at cutoff and the negative AC alternations will increase the bias even further. On positive half-cycles, however, amplifier current will flow, the average amount of current causing a proportional deflection of the meter pointer.

This simple triode circuit is not used in practical VTVM's however, mainly because if the voltage to be measured exceeded the bias voltage, the grid would draw current, loading the circuit under test, and resulting in an inaccurate indication on the meter. Another reason is that the probe may be connected only to a positive voltage; there is no provision for measuring negative voltage.

Practical VTVM Circuit

The basic circuit used in many VTVM's is shown in Fig. 6-6. The arrangement in Fig. 6-6A is for measurement of positive voltage. The circuit in Fig. 6-6B (the same as the one in Fig. 6-6A except for the point to which the probe is connected) is for measurement of negative voltage.

The basic vacuum-tube voltmeter circuit of Fig. 6-6 is known as a bridge circuit—the meter movement is "bridged" between the plates of two identical vacuum tube circuits. Suppose no voltage is being measured, the grids of V1 and V2 are at the same potential, with no grid voltage applied to V1. Under this condition the currents through the tubes are equal, and their plates are at the same potential. With the same potential at each side of the meter, no current flows through the meter, so the pointer indicates zero. If it does not indicate zero, the ZERO ADJUST control is adjusted so that the indication is zero.

VTVM DC VOLTAGE MEASUREMENT

When the test leads in Fig. 6-6A are connected across a source of voltage, with the probe connected to the more posi-

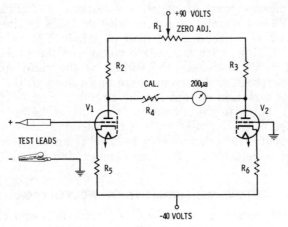

(A) Measuring positive DC voltage.

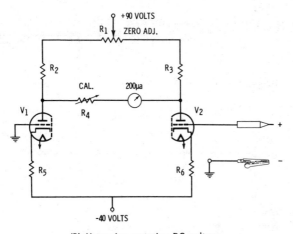

(B) Measuring negative DC voltage.

Fig. 6-6. Practical amplifier circuit for VTVM.

tive point, the current through V1 increases, causing a voltage drop in R2, thus decreasing the voltage on the left side of the meter movement. With the right side of the meter now more positive than the left, current flows through the meter, its value proportional to the voltage applied to the grid of V1. The current in V2 does not change, since its grid is grounded. The calibration (CAL) control in series with the meter is not an operating control; it is adjusted only at the time of calibration of the meter for exact indication of the pointer.

For measurement of negative voltage, a switching circuit in the VTVM usually transfers the test leads to the opposite triode V2 and grounds the grid of triode V1, as shown in Fig. 6-6B. Now, with a negative voltage on the probe tip, the current in V2 decreases, the voltage at the right side of the meter increases, and current again flows through the meter in the same direction as that for the circuit in Fig. 6-6A.

As is shown in the schematic, the voltage being measured is applied to the input of each of the vacuum tubes, not to the meter itself. Thus, the meter is isolated from the circuit under test and is relatively safe from damage due to overload.

VTVM MEASUREMENT OF AC VOLTAGE

For the measurement of AC voltage, the same circuit of Fig. 6-6 is used but is preceded by a rectifier circuit (Fig.

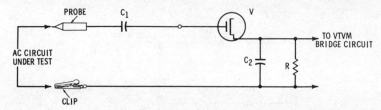

(A) Basic half wave rectifier circuit.

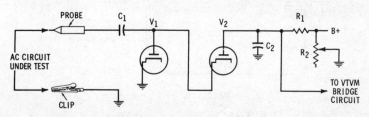

(B) Full-wave peak-to-peak rectifier circuit.

Fig. 6-7. VTVM rectifier circuits for AC voltage measurement.

6-7A). When AC voltage at the probe swings positive, diode V conducts through resistance R, at the same time charging capacitor C to the peak value of the AC input voltage. Resistor R is of high value, so C does not discharge completely before the next half-cycle charges it again. The voltage to the grid of the bridge amplifier is approximately equal to the peak value of the AC input voltage.

Often the rectifier for AC voltage measurement in a VTVM is a twin-diode peak-to-peak rectifier, similar to that shown in Fig. 6-7B. When the AC input voltage goes positive, capacitor C1 charges through diode V1 to the peak value of the positive voltage.

As the AC voltage swings through zero toward negative, V1 stops conducting; C1 remains charged to the peak voltage, since it has no discharge path. With the input signal now negative, C1 discharges through diode V2 which conducts through C2. The charge on C2 is now the sum of its charge and that of C1, or, the total of the positive and negative peaks. Thus, the rectifier circuit provides the grid or input of the bridge circuit with a peak-to-peak voltage for the deflection of the meter movement. This scale, however, will be calibrated in terms of rms for a sine-wave voltage and, sometimes, for peak and peak-to-peak values. Potentiometer R2 permits adjustment for zero deflection of the pointer when a zero volt input is applied.

VTVM RESISTANCE MEASUREMENT

For measurement of resistance, the input circuit to the VTVM bridge is basically that shown in Fig. 6-8A. When the test leads are shorted together, there will be no deflection of the pointer—a zero-ohms calibration control (not shown here) is adjusted for 0 ohms reading. Then, with the test leads open, the 1.5-volt battery in series with R1 is across the input circuit, and the meter is deflected full scale (adjusted exactly by means of an Ohms Adjust control, not shown here). When the test leads are then connected across an unknown resistor R_x, the deflection of the pointer will be in proportion to the value of R_x. Thus, in the VTVM, as is apparent on the Ohms (top) scale of the VTVM faceplate of Fig. 6-9, that the greater is the resistance, the greater is the deflection. This is opposite to the effect in the VOM, where deflection of the pointer is less when the resistance value of the unknown resistance is increased.

In Fig. 6-8A, when the unknown resistance has the same value as R1, the deflection is midscale, since R1 and R_x then form a 2:1 voltage divider, that applies half the battery voltage to the input circuit of the bridge.

Shown in Fig. 6-8B is the same circuit, but with a switch and additional resistors added for providing 6 resistance-measurement ranges. In position 1 of Switch S, the midscale reading of the VTVM is 10 megohms; in position 2, the midscale reading is 1 megohm; in position 3 it is 100K, and so on to the highest range.

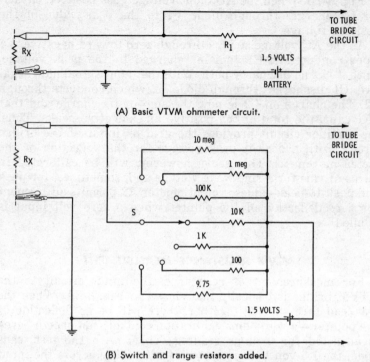

(A) Basic VTVM ohmmeter circuit.

(B) Switch and range resistors added.

Fig. 6-8. VTVM resistance measuring circuit.

VTVM CURRENT MEASUREMENT

The facility to measure current is not usually provided in a VTVM, although some models do include this facility. One of the advantages of a VTVM is that a less-sensitive meter

Fig. 6-9. Example of VTVM meter faceplate showing differences from the VOM.

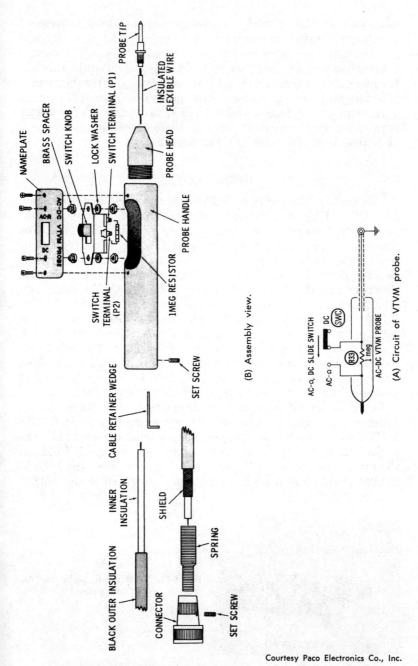

(B) Assembly view.

(A) Circuit of VTVM probe.

Courtesy Paco Electronics Co., Inc.

Fig. 6-10. Circuit of single probe for measurement of AC, DC, and ohms.

89

movement can be utilized; another is that the meter movement is relatively safe from accidental overload. VTVM's designed for current measurement therefore cannot usually measure currents as low as the average VOM. Also, to provide a means for measuring current in a VTVM increases greatly the chance of accidental damage to the meter movement.

In some of the late model VTVM's, protection to the meter is provided in the form of a zener diode across the movement, or a fuse in series with the movement.

VTVM PROBES

The basic probe for most VTVMs is as previously described. For DC voltage measurement it consists of a housing that contains a 1-megohm resistor in series with the test lead. For the measurement of AC voltage and for the measurement of resistance, the 1-megohm series resistor is not used. So either another probe is used, or a switch is included in the probe for shorting out the 1-megohm resistor in the AC voltage and ohm functions. The circuit of a typical probe is shown in Fig. 6-10A, with the switch in the DC volts position (1-megohm resistor in the circuit). In the opposite position of the switch used for AC and ohms, the 1-megohm resistor is shorted out. An assembly view of this probe is shown in Fig. 6-10B. The probe and VTVM are shown in Fig. 6-11. The probe coaxial jack and the common-lead jack are at the lower left.

For the measurement of high frequency AC voltage, an additional probe that is called an RF probe may be utilized with a VTVM. In an RF probe, a diode is built directly into the probe. In this way, capacitive loading from the VTVM on the circuit under test is kept at a minimum; also, the VTVM is able to measure a higher frequency range since the output

Fig. 6-11. VTVM single probe for AC, DC and ohms.

Courtesy Paco Electronics Co., Inc.

90

from the probe diode is DC voltage. Therefore, the capacitance of the cable and the VTVM input circuit has no reactive attenuating effect on the signal being measured.

The VTVM, like the VOM, can also be used to measure voltages greater than those for which it was basically designed. This is done by means of a high-voltage multiplier probe (Fig. 6-12). This probe is similar to the VOM high-voltage probe described earlier. Because of the higher average input resistance of the VTVM, a VTVM high-voltage probe has considerably less loading effect on a high-resistance, high-voltage circuit than does the VOM high-voltage probe.

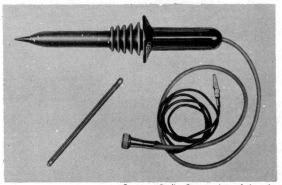

Courtesy Radio Corporation of America

Fig. 6-12. High voltage probe showing also high voltage multiplier resistor used.

For a VTVM having an 11-megohm input resistance, the value of the series multiplier resistor, which is in the handle of the high voltage probe, is 1,089 megohms for a 100:1 voltage reduction. The 1,089 megohms adds to the 11-megohm input resistance of the VTVM, giving a voltage divider having 1,100-megohms total input resistance. The input to the 11-megohm VTVM measuring circuit is 1/100 of the high-voltage being measured. The probe may be used on any of the VTVM voltage ranges where the input resistance is 11-megohms.

RESPONSE OF VTVM

The VTVM has a wider frequency response than the VOM. A typical VTVM with general-purpose probes provides a flat response within 1 db or so from 20 or 30 cps to 3 or 4 mc or more. With an RF probe, the response can be extended to 250 mc or more. For some laboratory VTVM's, this response extends to 1,000 mc.

TYPICAL VTVM CIRCUIT

At this point a brief examination of an actual VTVM circuit will help unite the basic concepts previously covered, for a better overall understanding of the operation of the VTVM. The VTVM we shall consider here is the Precision Model 48 shown in Fig. 6-13; the schematic is shown in Fig. 6-14. This model is in fairly wide use, its circuit is typical, and the schematic is drawn in an uncomplicated form.

Fig. 6-13. Precision Model 48 VTVM.

Courtesy Precision Apparatus Co., Inc.

The input to this VTVM is by means of a common-purpose probe (AC/DC/Ohms), with a 1-megohm series resistor that is used in the DC volts position of the slide switch. In the schematic, the four-wafer range switch is shown in the 1.5-volt position, and the four-wafer function switch is shown in the Off position. The 6AL5 twin diode, V1, is the peak-to-peak, full-wave rectifier employed for AC voltage measurement. The 12AU7 double-triode, V2, circuit is the vacuum-tube bridge. Note that there is a difference between the double-triode bridge circuit previously discussed and the one shown here. In Fig. 6-14, the grid of right-hand triode V2 is continuously grounded through a 4.7-megohm resistor, and the input is always applied to the grid of the left-hand triode. The reversal necessary for reading plus (+) and minus (−) input voltages is obtained by reversing the meter when going from (+) to (−), instead of changing grid connections. Another noticeable difference exists here, as compared with the basic circuit considered earlier. Here the meter is connected between the cathodes of

92

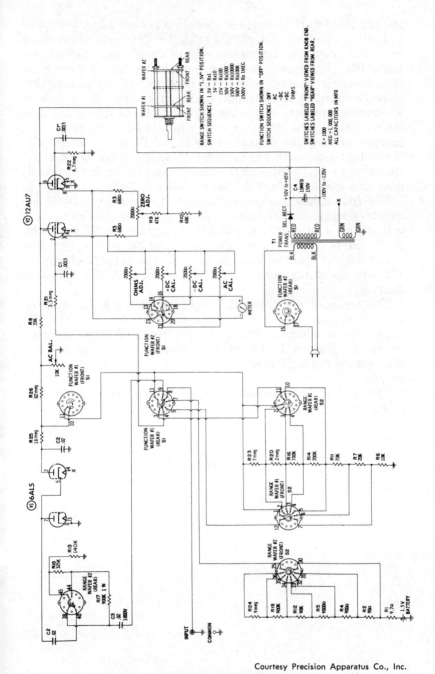

Courtesy Precision Apparatus Co., Inc.

Fig. 6-14. Schematic of Precision Model 48 VTVM.

the two triodes. However, the operation is basically the same— a positive input voltage on the grid, pin 2, causes an increase in current flow, increasing the voltage drop across cathode resistor R3. This makes the voltage at the top of R3 more positive, creating unequal voltages at each side of the meter. This causes current to flow through the meter, deflecting the pointer an amount proportional to the applied voltage. For a negative input-voltage, the effect is just opposite—plate current decreases, making the voltage at the top of R3 less positive. The current now flows in the opposite direction in the circuit, but the same direction through the meter, since the meter terminals have now been reversed by the function switch.

The four 2,000-ohm controls are calibration controls for accurate setting of the pointer for the resistance, minus DC voltage, plus DC voltage, and AC voltage scales. The AC balance control (top center) is also a calibration control. Only the Ohms Adjust and the Zero Adjust (in the cathode circuit of V2) are operating controls on the front panel of the instrument.

The series of resistors, R24, R18, R12, R5, R4, R2, and the 1.5-volt battery at the lower left of the schematic form the resistance measuring circuit. To the right of these, another series of resistors, R23, R20, R16, R14, R11, R7, and R6, are the voltage-multiplier resistors for the AC and DC voltage ranges.

The VTVM is supplied by a transformer selenium-rectifier power supply.

Chapter 7

Inside the VTVM

It is time to examine the internal features of some typical VTVM's and to point out the important features of representative instruments.

LAFAYETTE KT-174

The VTVM shown in Fig. 7-1 is similar in most respects to instruments already considered; for the most part, it utilizes the basic circuits and components. Some circuit refinements are included, however, and the major ones are pointed out later. The instrument may be obtained either in kit form or prewired. It is suitable for some laboratory-type measurements and for industrial and service applications.

In the front view shown, the coaxial input jack for an AC/DC/ohms cable and probe, is at the lower right of the meter movement. The Ohms Adjust and Zero Adjust controls are at the upper and lower right of the meter face. The Range

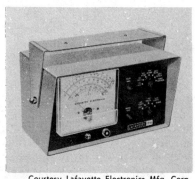

Fig. 7-1. Front view, Lafayette
KT-174 VTVM.

Courtesy Lafayette Electronics Mfg. Corp.

and Function switches are at the upper and lower right of the front panel.

Shown in Fig. 7-2 is an internal view of this VTVM, with most of the major components identified. For comparison, a schematic of the circuit is shown in Fig. 7-3.

A series of calibration and balance-control potentiometers is provided along the rear panel. Also on the rear panel, at the

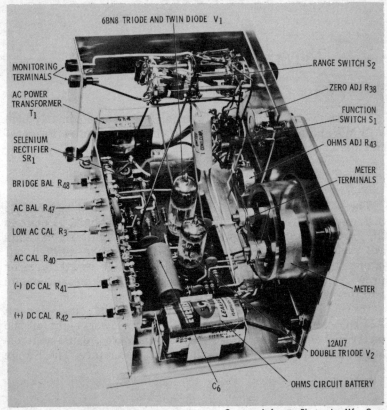

6BN8 TRIODE AND TWIN DIODE V_1

MONITORING TERMINALS

AC POWER TRANSFORMER T_1

SELENIUM RECTIFIER SR_1

BRIDGE BAL R_{48}

AC BAL R_{47}

LOW AC CAL R_3

AC CAL R_{40}

(-) DC CAL R_{41}

(+) DC CAL R_{42}

RANGE SWITCH S_2

ZERO ADJ R_{38}

FUNCTION SWITCH S_1

OHMS ADJ R_{43}

METER TERMINALS

METER

12AU7 DOUBLE TRIODE V_2

OHMS CIRCUIT BATTERY

C_6

Courtesy Lafayette Electronics Mfg. Corp.

Fig. 7-2. Internal construction of Lafayette KT-174 VTVM.

upper left in Fig. 7-2, is a pair of monitoring terminals. These terminals are connected across the input of the VTVM and may be used for plugging in an oscilloscope for monitoring a waveform while taking voltage measurements and making circuit adjustments. The Range Switch S2 is a 3-deck, 6-wafer switch, with the individual sections labeled S2a through S2f in the schematic. The Function Switch S1 is a 2-deck, 4-wafer

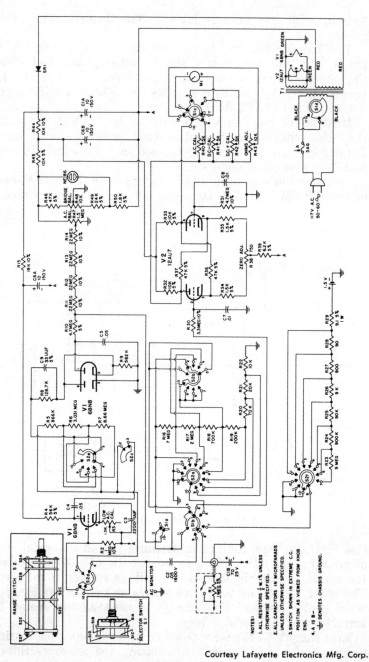

Courtesy Lafayette Electronics Mfg. Corp.

Fig. 7-3. Schematic of Lafayette KT-174 VTVM.

switch, with its sections labeled S1a through S1d in the schematic.

The battery for the Ohms circuit, bottom center in the photo, is a 1.5-volt standard size-D battery. Identified also in the photo are the meter and meter terminals, and the two vacuum tubes, V1, which is a 6BN8 triode and twin diode, and V2, which is a 12AU7 double triode.

Most of the smaller components in this VTVM, as well as the tube sockets, are mounted on a printed circuit board. Printed circuits are now widely used in VOM's and VTVM's, and they give good results.

Consider the schematic briefly, along with a block diagram of this VTVM, Fig. 7-4, for some features not yet covered in

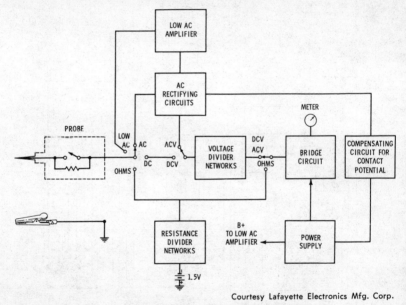

Courtesy Lafayette Electronics Mfg. Corp.

Fig. 7-4. Block diagram of Lafayette KT-174-VTVM.

this text. One new item of importance is that a special stage of amplification (the triode section of the 6BN8) is provided for making available several low voltage ranges, 0 to .5 volt. The other section of the 6BN8 serves as the twin-diode, full-wave peak rectifier. The 12AU7 is used as the meter DC amplifier and balanced bridge.

Most early VTVM's were powered by a vacuum-tube rectifier power supply, but in recent instruments, the power rectifier is a selenium type (Figs. 7-2 and 7-3) or a silicon type.

RCA SENIOR VOLTOHMYST WV98-C

For further consideration of external details of VTVM's some of the features of the RCA WV-98C Senior VoltOhmyst are shown in Fig. 7-5. The AC/DC/ohms probe and common (or ground) cable and clip are in the foreground. The front panel controls are, left to right, the range switch, the Zero Adjust control, the Ohms Adjust control, and the function switch. Just above the bottom center of the VTVM, and above where the cable jack is connected, is located a snap-in cover beneath which is located the zero adjustment for the

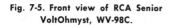

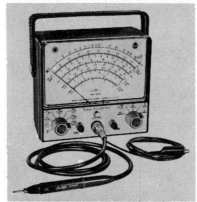

Fig. 7-5. Front view of RCA Senior VoltOhmyst, WV-98C.

Courtesy Radio Corporation of America

pointer. Though the entire instrument is fairly small and compact, the meter face is fairly large, about 7 inches × 4 inches. Two Low AC scales, one peak to peak scale, one DC or rms scale, and one ohms scale are provided, with two sets of calibrated figures for each of the voltage scales. The pilot lamp in the upper left corner of the meter faceplate indicates when the VTVM is Off.

In the Off position of the function switch (marked Off Transit), a short is connected across the meter terminals, damping its movement. This prevents damage to the pointer and movement when the VTVM is not being used.

A rear view of the VTVM of Fig. 7-5 is shown in Fig. 7-6A. The case cover has been removed to show the rear view of the printed circuit board. Barely visible on the laminated board are four calibrate controls for AC Zero, −DC, AC, and +DC. These controls are not accessible through the rear of the instrument case; the instrument must be removed from the case for calibration. The intent of the manufacturer in the design was to provide an instrument as stable as possible and to place the calibration controls so that they would not be accidentally disturbed. The cover is removed by removing four slotted machine screws on the back of the cover. These are visible in Fig. 7-6B. Also visible in this view in Fig. 7-6B are the ohms-circuit battery, the 12AU7 bridge-amplifier tube, and the function switch.

(A) View of printed circuit board.

(B) Showing location of function switch, battery and tube.

Courtesy Radio Corporation of America

Fig. 7-6. Rear views of RCA Senior VoltOhmyst, WV-98C.

A schematic of the WV-98C Senior VoltOhmyst is shown in Fig. 7-7. Note that the circuit, Fig. 7-7, is quite similar in most respects to the basic circuits discussed earlier. The meter circuit is located between the plates of the two triodes of the 12AU7. The 6AL5 is a peak-to-peak, full-wave rectifier circuit, and a 200-microampere movement is employed. The ohms-circuit multiplier resistors are connected to the contacts of S2A, and the voltage multiplier resistors are connected to S2C. Since, on the schematic, both switches are shown in the

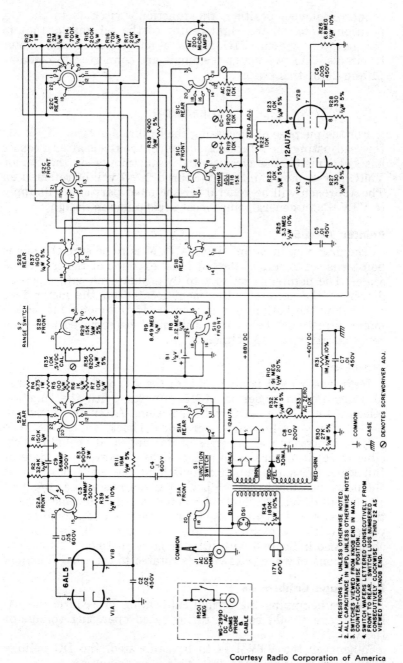

Courtesy Radio Corporation of America

Fig. 7-7. Schematic diagram of RCA Senior VoltOhmyst, WV-98C.

counterclockwise position, the function switch is in the Off position. Note, on the right center of the schematic, that in the position shown, S1C places a short across the meter terminals. The two meter terminals are connected to contacts 11 and 20 of this switch.

CALIBRATION

For the purpose of discussing the calibration of a VTVM, or for readjusting the internal and external controls after a repair has been made, the circuits and adjustments of the Senior VoltOhmyst, shown in Figs. 7-5 through 7-7 will be referred to. The approach will be general for the most part and will apply to VTVM's in general, since most are similar in design.

Pointer Zero Set

The first step in calibrating a VTVM is to be sure the meter pointer is set to zero at the left-hand extreme of the calibrated scales. The pointer is set to zero by adjustment with a screwdriver of the zero-set adjustment located on the meter face just below the bottom of the pointer. If the meter includes a meter-adjustment hole cover, this must be removed and then replaced after the adjustment.

Warm-up

Next, the VTVM is plugged into the AC outlet and allowed to warm-up for a period of 15 minutes, with the function selector set to the +DC volts position. After the warm-up period, for a preliminary operational check, rotate the Zero Adjust control to the extremes of its ranges; it should be possible to set it at zero or to deflect it to 60 percent or more of full-scale. With the function switch in the −DC position, it should be possible to set the pointer to zero as well as to about 10 percent deflection point. If it is not possible to come close to these results possibly the 12AU7 is defective and should be replaced. With the pointer set to zero on the +DC function, it should also indicate 0 with little or no adjustment of the Zero Adjust control when the switch is rotated to the −DC function.

DC Voltage Calibration

Before beginning the formal calibration procedure, the AC line voltage should be close to the rated operating voltage of the VTVM.

Whenever the VTVM is to be calibrated, the DC voltage calibration must be made first. This is as follows:

First, in the +DC volts position, after 30 minutes of warm-up, set the Zero Adjust for exactly 0 as shown in Fig. 7-9. Next, with the range switch set to 50 volts, connect the ground (or common cable clip) and the probe (set to DC volts) across a voltage source of exactly 50 volts. The probe should be attached to the positive voltage point. Next, with a screwdriver, set the DC Calibration potentiometer to bring the pointer exactly to full-scale deflection, the 50-volt mark on the DC scale.

Reverse the test-lead positions to the 50-volt source, first setting the function switch to the −DC position; then adjust the −DC Calibrate so that the pointer again indicates exactly 50 volts. All other DC voltage ranges should now be accurate when checked against other known DC voltages.

Low DC Voltage-Range Calibration

Some VTVM's have a calibration control for the 0.5-volt DC range. The calibration for this range is generally as follows. Set the Function switch to +DC. With the range switch in the 0.5-volt position, set the Zero Adjust to exactly zero deflection. Connect the probe to the positive end of a source of exactly 0.5 volt DC and the common lead to the negative side. Set the 0.5 volt DC calibrate control for exactly full-scale deflection, which is at the 5.0 mark on the 0 to 5 DC volts scale.

AC Voltage Calibration

After the DC voltage calibration has been completed, the VTVM may be calibrated for the AC voltage ranges. Set the probe switch to AC or AC/ohms, the function switch to AC volts, and the range switch to 1.5 volts. To make sure that no nearby electrical fields will induce a voltage into the probe and cable, connect the ground clip to the probe tip, shorting out the VTVM input circuit. Set the AC Zero Calibrate control for exactly zero deflection. If the pointer cannot be zeroed, the twin-diode rectifier may be defective and should be replaced.

Assuming that the pointer can be zeroed exactly, connect the probe and ground clip across a source of exactly 50 volts AC, 60 cps. If the pointer does not indicate exactly 50 volts on the AC range, adjust the AC Calibrate control so that the meter reads exactly 50 volts. This completes the AC calibration.

Ohms Calibration

Before calibration of the Ohms function of the VTVM, it is good practice to be sure that a fresh battery is in the instrument. A weak battery may at first permit proper performance of the instrument but the output of the battery may drop during the course of the calibration, causing an inaccurate calibration for resistance measurements.

For the ohms calibration, set the function switch to the +DC volts position, and make sure that the pointer is at zero— if not, set the Zero Adjust control to give the zero setting. Next, set the function switch to the ohms position, the Range switch to R × 1, and the Ohms Adjust control for full-scale (∞) deflection. Set the Range switch to the R × 1 Meg position. Without disturbing any adjustment, the pointer should come to the 1,000 mark, or above, on the resistance scale. If it does not come up to the 1,000 mark, this is an indication of leakage in the ohms circuit of the VTVM.

When going from a low range to the R × 1 range, it will be necessary to reset the Ohms Adjust control for accurate results. Replacement of the 12AU7 tube may correct this condition. If it is not possible to obtain a full-scale setting on any range with the Ohm Adjust control, the battery probably is weak and should be replaced.

Whenever a tube is replaced in the VTVM, it should be aged 30 to 50 hours before calibration of the instrument; meanwhile the VTVM can be used, remembering that the results might not be at the rated accuracy of the instrument.

Other VTVM's having special circuits or extended ranges will differ somewhat from the calibration procedure given here. For these instruments, and for all instruments the directions of the manufacturer should be followed exactly.

USING THE VTVM

Before using the VTVM, it should be allowed to warm-up at least 5 minutes; but, for accuracy, 20 to 30 minutes would be better. It would be impossible to give specific descriptions of how to use all VTVM's in this book; this information is provided in the Operating Manual for each instrument. However, a general procedure can be given, and will apply to the average VTVM.

Identification of VTVM Scales

For a detailed identification of the scales of a VTVM, see Fig. 7-8. Scale R is used for all resistance measurements; the values indicated by the pointer are multiplied by factors of 1, 10, 100, etc., depending on the position of the Range switch. Scales A and B are used for all DC voltage measurements and for all AC voltage measurements except on the 0 to 1.5 volts and the 0 to 0.5 volt scales. These ranges are measured on the G and E scales, respectively. Scales C and D are used for all AC peak-to-peak voltage measurements, except for the 0 to 4 volt AC range and the 0 to 14 volt AC range; these are measured on scales H and F respectively.

Triplett Model 850; Zero-Center Scale

Another VTVM, the Triplett Model 850, is shown in Fig. 7-9. The scales of this instrument are only slightly different from those of the VTVM's already described. Except for the bottom scale, the only noticeable difference is in the order of arrangement for the low AC scales. The bottom scale is a zero-center

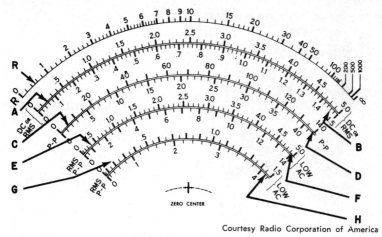

Fig. 7-8. Identification of meter scales.

scale, calibrated up to −45 on the left and +45 on the right. It is intended mainly for use in the alignment of FM receiver discriminators. In this application, as receiver adjustments are made, plus and minus voltages are indicated as the circuit is tuned toward a zero voltage reading. Other VTVM's also have a zero-center indication marked below their scales, and are usable for zero-center measurements. For quantitative readings, the scale indications must be converted mentally.

To use the zero-center scale of a VTVM, the Zero Adjust control is used to move the pointer to the center of the scale. Then, negative voltage readings will swing the pointer to the left and positive voltage to the right. On a VTVM in which a specific scale is not calibrated left and right from zero, the relative readings can be easily computed mentally. For example on a 0- to 15-volt scale, the center would be 7.5 volts—this would be considered zero. The value 7.5 would be subtracted from readings to the left of center. The actual value of a reading of 5.0 volts would be 5.0 volts − 7.5 volts = −2.5 volts. Similarly, the value 7.5 is subtracted from readings above center. If the indication is 8.0 volts the actual value is 8.0 volts − 7.5 volts = 0.5 volt.

DC Voltage Measurements

The procedure for using a VTVM, for the measurement of DC voltages are given for the meter shown in Fig. 7-9, but the same general procedure applies to practically any VTVM, with only minor differences.

Fig. 7-9. Triplett Model 850 VTVM.

Courtesy Triplett Electrical Instrument Co.

Connect the plug of the probe cable to the instrument, plug the VTVM into the AC outlet, and allow it to warm up for the required time. Adjust the zero-adjust control for zero indication. For this adjustment it is recommended that the probe tip be connected to the clip of the common lead to prevent stray pickup from creating a deflection of the pointer. Turn the function selector to the ohms position, and adjust for full-scale deflection with the ohms adjust control. Set the probe slide switch to the DC position and the function switch to +DC or −DC, as required. Set the Range switch to a higher voltage range than you expect to measure. Connect the common clip to the ground, chassis, or low potential side of the voltage to be measured. Connect the probe tip to the high potential side of the circuit. Then, if necessary, set the Range switch to a position that gives a reading nearest full scale. The voltage is then read from the scale that corresponds to the range setting of the range switch.

Resistance Measurements

For resistance measurements, the probe switch should be in the AC/OHMS position. Set the range switch to the R × 10 position, short the probe tip to the ground clip, and adjust the Zero Adjust to set the pointer to the left hand 0. Separate the probe tip from the ground clip, making sure you are not touching either clip. Adjust the Ohms Adjust for full-scale deflection. Connect the ground clip to one lead of the resistance to be measured and the probe tip to the other lead. Some VTVM's are provided with an alligator clip that may be attached to the end of the probe tip. The clip then may be connected to the resistor while the resistance measurement is being made. If necessary, reset the Range switch to give a convenient deflection—somewhere near the center (or higher) on the ohms scale. If the range switch is set, for example, to R × 100, and the scale indication is 15, the actual resistance being measured is 1,500 ohms. Similarly, with the Range switch on R × 1K and an indication of 20, the value of the resistance being measured is 20,000 ohms.

AC Voltage Measurement

For the measurement of AC voltage, the probe switch is set to AC/ohms, the range switch to AC, the Zero Adjust control for 0 indication of the pointer, and the ground clip is connected to the chassis, common, or low-potential point of the AC voltage being measured. Select a voltage range higher than that which you expect to measure; then connect the probe tip to the high potential side of the AC voltage being measured. Then, if necessary, set the Range switch to give a convenient reading, with the pointer in the upper ⅔ of the scale. Read the pointer indication on the scale corresponding to the range being used. Be sure to read from the proper AC scale, if you are using one of the Low AC ranges, or whether or not you want to read rms or peak-to-peak. On some VTVM's the rms scales are colored black, and the peak-to-peak scales are colored red.

Measuring Decibels

For the measurement of db (Output), set up the VTVM as described for AC Volts measurement. If the voltage measured is across a 600-ohm line, the chart shown in Fig. 7-10 may be used for converting the AC rms voltage reading to db with the 0-db reference of 1 mw. As an example of using this chart, if you measure, say, 10 AC rms volts across a resistance or

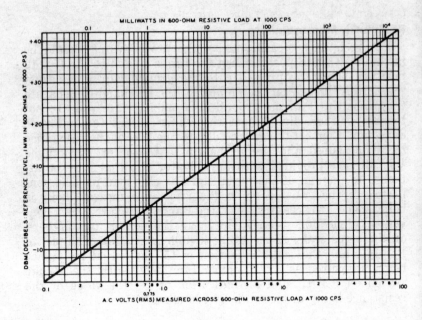

Fig. 7-10. Graph relating dbm to AC rms voltages.

line of 600 ohms, the equivalent value is 22 dbm; similarly, 2 AC rms volts across 600 ohms is equal to 8 dbm, etc.

For circuits other than 600 ohms, the Table 7-1 may be employed to determine the correction factor. For instance, if we measure 20 AC rms volts, the chart shows this to be equal to about 28 dbm for a 600-ohm circuit; but if the measurement is made across a 150-ohm circuit, the table indi-

Table 7-1. Correction Factor, $10 \log \dfrac{600}{R}$

RESISTIVE LOAD AT 1000 CPS	DBM*
600	0
500	+0.8
300	+3.0
250	+3.8
150	+6.0
50	+10.8
15	+16.0
8	+18.8
3.2	+22.7

* DBM is the increment to be added algebraically to the dbm value read from Fig. 7-10.

Courtesy Triplett Electrical Instrument Co.

cates that we must add 6 dbm—the actual value then is 28 + 6, or 34 dbm.

For circuits other than 600 ohms, not shown in the table, the formula shown below the table may be used; in the formula, R represents the resistance of the circuit in which the measurement is made. If R is higher than 600 ohms, the correction factor is negative. For instance, suppose we measure 9 AC rms volts across 6,000 ohms. From the graph of Fig. 7-10, it is noted that 9 AC rms volts in a 600-ohm circuit is 21 dbm. The correction factor which must be added (subtracted, in this case, since 6,000 is higher than 600) is:

$$\text{Correction factor} = 10 \log \frac{600}{6,000}$$
$$= 10 \log 0.1 = 10 \times (-1)$$
$$= -10 \text{ dbm.}$$

Thus, the dbm equivalent of 9 AC rms volts across 6,000 ohms is 21 − 10, or 11 dbm.

Operation Chart

Most instruction manuals for VTVM's include an operation chart, such as that shown in Table 7-2, which condenses the instructions for the settings of the function, range, and probe switches, and indicates the scale to be used and the multiplier for AC/DC, or resistance measurement within the range of the VTVM. When you purchase a new VTVM or use one for the first time, the operations chart should not be overlooked. It can speed your obtaining a familiarity with the instrument. For instance, suppose you plan to measure peak-to-peak volts of more than 1,400 but less than 4,000 volts. From the chart you can see that you should set the range switch at 4,000, the function switch at AC-PP, the probe switch at AC-Ohms, obtain the reading from the Red 0-40 PP scale, and multiply the scale reading by 100.

Table 7-2. Operation Chart for Triplett Model 850 VTVM

TO MEASURE	SET RANGE SWITCH AT	SET FUNCTION SWITCH AT	PROBE SWITCH POSITION	READ ON SCALE	SCALE	REMARKS
DC Volts				**Black Scales**		
0-.5	.5	DC VOLTS	DC	0-50 DC	÷ by 100	See instructions for DC Volts measurements. Be sure probe switch is in DC position.
0-1.5	1.5	DC VOLTS	DC	0-15 DC	÷ by 10	
0-5	5	DC VOLTS	DC	0-50 DC	÷ by 10	
0-15	15	DC VOLTS	DC	0-15 DC	Read Direct	
0-50	50	DC VOLTS	DC	0-50 DC	Read Direct	
0-150	150	DC VOLTS	DC	0-15 DC	X 10	
0-500	500	DC VOLTS	DC	0-50 DC	X 10	
0-1500	1500	DC VOLTS	DC	0-15 DC	X 100	
AC-RMS				**Black Scales**		
0-1.5	1.5	AC-RMS	AC-OHMS	0-1.5 AC	Direct	See instructions for AC RMS measurements.
0-5	5	AC-RMS	AC-OHMS	0-5 AC	Direct	
0-15	15	AC-RMS	AC-OHMS	0-15 AC	Direct	
0-50	50	AC-RMS	AC-OHMS	0-50 AC	Direct	
0-150	150	AC-RMS	AC-OHMS	0-15 AC	X 10	
0-500	500	AC-RMS	AC-OHMS	0-50 AC	X 10	
0-1500	1500	AC-RMS	AC-OHMS	0-15 AC	X 100	
OHMS				**Top Scale OHMS**		
0-1000	R X 1	OHMS	AC-OHMS	0-1000 OHMS	Read Direct	See instructions for resistance measurements. Be sure probe switch is in OHM position.
0-10,000	R X 10	OHMS	AC-OHMS	0-1000 OHMS	X 10	
0-100,000	R X 100	OHMS	AC-OHMS	0-1000 OHMS	X 100	
0-1,000,000	R X 1K	OHMS	AC-OHMS	0-1000 OHMS	X 1K	
0-10,000,000	R X 10K	OHMS	AC-OHMS	0-1000 OHMS	X 10K	
0-100 Meg.	R X 100K	OHMS	AC-OHMS	0-1000 OHMS	X 100K	
0-1000 Meg.	R X 1 Meg.	OHMS	AC-OHMS	0-1000 OHMS	X 1 Meg.	

Peak to Peak

			Red Scales	
4	AC-PP	AC-OHMS	0-4 PP	Read Direct
14	AC-PP	AC-OHMS	0-14 PP	Read Direct
40	AC-PP	AC-OHMS	0-40 PP	Read Direct
140	AC-PP	AC-OHMS	0-140 PP	Read Direct
400	AC-PP	AC-OHMS	0-40 PP	X 10
1400	AC-PP	AC-OHMS	0-140 PP	X 10
4000	AC-PP	AC-OHMS	0-40 PP	X 100

See instructions for Peak to Peak voltage measurement.

Decibels

See Chart −26 to +40	1.5	AC-RMS	AC-OHMS	Black AC Scales
	5	AC-RMS	AC-OHMS	
	15	AC-RMS	AC-OHMS	
	50	AC-RMS	AC-OHMS	
	150	AC-RMS	AC-OHMS	

See instructions for Decibel measurements.

Courtesy Triplett Electrical Instrument Co.

Chapter 8

Care of the VTVM

The comments regarding care and maintenance that apply to the VOM covered earlier in this book also apply, generally to the VTVM. To review briefly, for application to the VTVM, the following precautions should be observed. The VTVM should be calibrated properly before using it; batteries, when weak or leaking, should be replaced; precautions regarding safety (connect the common lead first, be careful of hot chassis equipment) should be followed; test leads should be kept in repair or not used if defective; safe storage location should be provided; locations near machinery, dust, dirt, excessive temperatures and humidity should be avoided; replacement fuses of same rating only should be used; replacement parts of the same characteristics and rating should be employed; repair of the meter movement should not be attempted.

In the next paragraphs additional items will be considered with regard to use and care, as they apply to the VTVM.

CAUSES OF FAILURE, OR INTERMITTENT OPERATION

Some causes of troubles in VTVMs are due to negligent or accidental misuse of the instrument. When you first notice something wrong with the VTVM, think back to the last time you used it for that particular function or range. You may possibly remember what you might have done wrong and will then be able to make repairs more quickly. You might have had the Function switch set for ohms when attempting to measure voltage. Noting that there was no voltage reading, you probably double-checked the switch settings, noticed that the function switch was not set to the voltage setting required, corrected this situation, and then proceeded with the voltage measurement, not realizing that you had burned out a resistor in the ohms circuit. In an accident of this sort, usually it is one of the low-value, ohms-multiplier resistors that opens. These would be the 9.45- and 95-ohm resistors. (Values may vary in different instruments.)

Many troubles are also due to failure of a component, tube, wiring, cable, switch or control. If trouble occurs, and you do not know where to start, the best approach is first to determine just which functions of the VTVM do not respond properly. Usually you can isolate the trouble to one or two major circuits. Begin by inspecting those parts, and checking over the voltages, resistances, etc. from the normal operating values as provided by the manufacturer's instruction manual.

Tube Failure

Occasionally a tube will fail in a VTVM. The result will be noticeable on the operation. The VTVM may fail to respond at all, will not calibrate properly, it may respond only on the AC voltage readings, or it may operate intermittently.

If you are unable to balance the VTVM, or if the balance is unstable, the cause may be the double triode (12AU7, ECC82, 7330, etc.), or the twin diode (6AL5). If there is no reading on any of the AC scales but DC readings are normal, the usual cause is a defective 6AL5; however, a defective rectifier unit could also cause this trouble. When tubes are replaced, the VTVM should be recalibrated as described in the instrument manual. Before final calibration, the tubes should be aged in the circuit, since their characteristics may change during the first few hours of operation. A tube can be pre-aged also, if you are anticipating a failure. Pre-aging can be done by applying 100 to 125 volts DC on the plate, connecting the grids and cathode together and to the −DC source, the filament to its rated voltage, and operating the tube in this manner for 40 to 50 hours. Then place the tube in the VTVM, and recalibrate.

Inaccurate Resistance Readings

If the resistance readings are inaccurate, it may be because the 1.5-volt battery is weak. A way to test the battery will be described later. If the battery does not prove to be weak, one or more resistors in the multiplier circuit may be open or off value—one symptom of a defective resistor is that resistance values measured on the lower Ohms ranges will creep in value—the reading will vary as you watch the pointer.

Other Causes of Failure of VTVM

Other causes of failure of the VTVM include a blown fuse, faulty on-off switch, open line cord, break in wiring, poor shield connection on probe cable, low power-supply DC voltage, and poor socket contacts.

Battery Test

To insure accuracy of resistance measurements, the battery should be tested now and then as follows.

Turn function selector to ohms. Set the range control to R × 1 position. Rotate the ohms adjust control for full-scale deflection of the pointer. Short the probe to the ground clip for about ten seconds. Open the circuit, and observe the indication. Any appreciable deviation from full-scale deflection indicates weak cells that should be replaced.

The reason the pointer may fail to deflect full scale is that with the prolonged short-circuiting of the probe tip to the ground clip, a fairly high current demand is placed on the battery. This lowers the voltage of a weak battery so that it does not permit full-scale deflection of the pointer when the short is removed.

SPECIAL APPLICATIONS

On most of the VTVM's described, the highest calibrated number on the scales is 1K. With the function switch on ohms and the range switch on 1 Megohm, the highest readable resistance is 1,000 megohms. On some rare occasions (or frequently in some cases) it may be necessary to measure a higher resistance. There is a way to do it using an external battery and series resistor, as shown in Fig. 8-1.

This method described by the manufacturer of the RCA WV98-C, which could apply directly, or with slight modification, to any comparable VTVM is as follows. The battery sym-

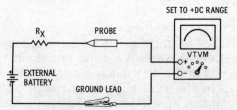

Fig. 8-1. Circuit showing use of VTVM to measure resistance beyond 1,000 megohms.

bol may represent an external voltage source of from 20 to 500 DC volts, whatever is required to make a deflection of the pointer. Connect the circuit, as shown and then:

1. Set function selector to +DC volts and measure the voltage at point B, Fig. 8-1.
2. Measure the voltage at point A, Fig. 8-1.
3. Compute the unknown resistance R_x from the following formula:

$$R_{x\,(megohms)} = \frac{11\,[(Volts\ at\ A) - (Volts\ at\ B)]}{(Volts\ at\ B)}$$

Example: The value of an unknown resistance is to be determined with the circuit of Fig. 8-1. An external voltage of 500 volts is applied. The WV-98C measures 2.5 volts at point B, and 500 volts at point A. Then,

$$R_x = \frac{11\,(500 - 2.5)}{2.5} = 2,200\ megohms\ approximately.$$

Peak-to-Peak Voltage Measurement

It has already been mentioned that the VTVM can be used to measure peak-to-peak voltages by reading directly from the peak-to-peak scales of the VTVM. In most cases, even for complex waves and other nonsinusoidal waves, the readings that are obtained will be accurate. In some cases, where the voltage wave being measured consists of pulses of very short duration, or pulses between which there is a long interval, the peak-to-peak voltage reading obtained will be lower than the actual value which would be accurately indicated by an oscilloscope.

High Frequency Measurement

The VTVM's previously discussed have responses up to 3 to 4 mc and down to 30 to 40 cps. For most VTVM's this response is accurate when the measurement is being made across a specific value of resistance such as 100 ohms, 600 ohms, 1,000 ohms, etc. For measurement across a circuit of some other resistance, the response may differ.

For example, a certain VTVM being flat to 4 mc when the measurement is made across 100 ohms, may be flat only to 500 kc when the measurement is made across 1,000 ohms. This possible deviation in response for circuits of different resistance should be remembered when making frequency response checks on audio and video amplifier circuits.

Fig. 8-2. VTVM with separate input jacks
for AC/DC/ohms probe and RF probe.

For making measurements of voltages having frequencies
above the specified response of the VTVM, the crystal diode
probe (available as an accessory for most VTVM's) should
be used. This will extend the response of the VTVM to 250 mc,
or more, depending on the VTVM and its associated probe. A
crystal diode probe sometimes is an additional cable and probe
that must be used instead of the AC/ohms/DC probe, or inserted in a different jack. The VTVM shown in Fig. 8-2 has
separate jacks for the standard and crystal diode (RF) probes.
In other cases, the crystal diode probe is simply placed over
the standard probe and used directly, as shown in Fig. 8-3.
This RCA WG-301A probe may be used in RF circuits to
measure sine-wave voltage values up to 20 rms volts in the
presence of DC voltage up to 250 volts. The range of the
probe is 50 kc to 250 mc. All RF voltages are read from the
DC scales in terms of rms volts for sine waves. For example:
A reading of 5 volts DC indicates that the sine wave being
measured has an rms value of 5 volts. The over-all accuracy
of the WV-98B when used with the WG-301A is ±10 percent.

Fig. 8-3. RCA WG-301A crystal-diode
probe used for high frequency voltage measurements.

Fig. 8-4. Example of combination VOM-
VTVM, Sencore SM112 Servicemaster.

Courtesy Sencore Inc.

ERRATIC VTVM READINGS DUE TO STATIC CHARGE

Some VTVM's (and VOM's) having plastic covers on the meter face may accumulate a charge of electricity when the cover is polished or cleaned. This may cause the pointer to deflect erratically whether the instrument is on or off. The static charges may easily be removed by using one of the commercially available anti-static solutions or a solution of any good liquid detergent and water. Dip a clean, soft cloth in the solution and wipe the surface of the meter cover. The cover need not be removed for this operation.

USE AND MAINTENANCE OF COMBINATION VTVM

Several manufacturers now offer combination VOM-VTVM's. An example of one, the SM112 Servicemaster, is shown in Fig. 8-4. Such an instrument may be used either as a VOM or as a VTVM, as required. Used as a VOM the instrument of Fig. 8-4 need not be plugged into an AC outlet. Resistance, current, and voltage measurements may be made as with any VOM. For higher resistance readings, or voltage measurements in high impedance circuits, the function selector is moved to the required VTVM function setting, and the measurements are continued. One additional feature of the instrument shown here is that the scale in use is identified directly by one of four lamps which light alongside the scale in use. Thus, possible error due to reading the wrong scale is reduced.

Troubleshooting a combination instrument is the same as for any other VOM or VTVM. In fact, the troubleshooting may be easier, since the VOM section can be checked out first, and if it operates, the trouble may be then limited to

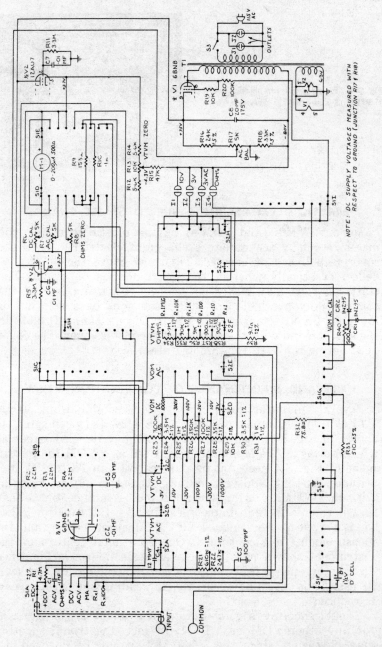

Courtesy Sencore Inc.

Fig. 8-5. Schematic of Sencore SM112 Servicemaster combination VOM-VTVM.

Table 8-1. Trouble Chart for the
SM112 SENCORE Servicemaster Combination VOM-VTVM

SYMPTOM	PROBABLE CAUSE	CORRECTIVE MEASURE
Meter does not indicate on DC milliamp check.	Burned out contacts on switch S1D or S1E due to excess current flow.	Clean contacts on switch; adjust contacts for increased pressure against rotor blade on switch.
VTVM and VOM volts do not work, everything else O.K.	Open resistor on DC divider network R23 through R33.	Check resistors using SM112 Ohmmeter.
Meter needle jumps excessively when switching functions.	Poor switch contacts on function switch S1C, S1F, S1G, S1J.	Clean and adjust contacts.
All scale indicating lamps do not light.	Poor switch contacts on function switch S11 or on range switch S2G, S2H.	Clean and adjust contacts.
Cannot set VTVM Zero to zero.	Defective 12AU7A.	Check both sections of tube; replace if bad.
VOM AC Volts does not work.	Defective 1N295 diode(s). Defective VOM Cal pot R40.	Check diodes for forward to reverse resistance using SM-112 ohmmeter. Check R40 with SM112 ohmmeter.
VTVM AC Volts does not work.	Defective 6BN8.	Check and replace if bad.
VTVM AC Volts reads up to 1 volt with no voltage applied.	AC pickup in test leads. AC balance pot misadjusted or setting changed due to tube aging or vibration.	Short test leads together and see if meter needle returns to zero. Adjust AC balance pot R17 to zero with test leads shorted together. Be sure that VTVM Zero was set correctly before making this adjustment.
No meter indication on any position of Function switch but meter lamps light.	Defect in switch S1A, S1D or S1E. Defective meter.	Check switch contacts. Clean if necessary. Check meter, if bad replace.
No meter indication on any VTVM position of Function switch but meter lamps light. VOM is O.K.	Defective 6BN8 or 12AU7A.	Replace if necessary.
No meter indication on any VTVM position of Function switch, meter lamps do not light.	Defective ON-OFF switch S3. Defective line cord or plug.	Check and replace if bad.

Table 8-1. Trouble Chart for the SM112 SENCORE Servicemaster Combination VOM-VTVM—Cont'd

SYMPTOM	PROBABLE CAUSE	CORRECTIVE MEASURE
Meter indications O.K. on all VTVM functions except ohms. VOM is O.K.	Open VTVM Ohms resistor. R39 most probable.	Check resistor using SM112 VOM ohms check. If resistor is open, replace.
Cannot adjust ohms zero on VTVM ohms. Other functions O.K.	Weak battery.	Check and replace if necessary.
Cannot adjust ohms zero on VTVM only. Other functions show low readings.	Defective 6BN8 or 12AU7A. Condenser C8.	Check tubes and replace if bad. Check condenser and replace if bad.

the VTVM circuits. In the instruction manual for this instrument, a trouble chart is provided, making it easier to locate and correct troubles that are likely to occur. The schematic diagram is shown in Fig. 8-5 so that controls, tube, components, etc. mentioned in the trouble chart may be located.

Chapter 9

Transistorized
Electronic Voltmeters

Transistorized versions of the VTVM are now available. Transistors offer the same advantages when used in an electronic measuring instrument as when used in any electronic equipment. These advantages include no warm-up time; reduced size and weight; no need to plug into AC outlet (thus the instrument can be used anywhere); practically no heat generated; and the potential advantage of greater stability.

Transistorized instruments are either completely transistorized or operate partly with transistors and partly with vacuum tubes.

DeVRY TRVM-1

The first example considers an all-transistor instrument. Study the circuit, and consider the special operating features. The instrument, the DeVry AC-DC Transistorized Multimeter TRVM-1 shown in Fig. 9-1, is much like a VTVM in appearance, having a Function switch, a Range switch, a pair of Input jacks, and a meter calibrated for Resistance, DC volts, DC microamperes, and AC volts. The main difference is that this instrument will measure very low values of current compared to a VTVM. The actual current ranges are 0 to 5, 0 to 50, 0 to 500, and 0 to 5,000 microamperes. A 0 to 500 milliampere range, or a 0 to 5 ampere range can be added by inserting an accessory shunt.

According to the manufacturer, the need to replace the transistors is practically nonexistent, mainly because stable, long-life transistors are used in the circuits, and these are operated considerably below their maximum rated values. The two switches shown are dual, concentric controls, as shown in

Fig. 9-1. The larger knob on the upper switch operates the range switch, and the smaller knob is the ohms adjust control. On the lower switch, the larger knob is the function switch, and the smaller is the zero adjust control.

The DC voltage ranges are 0 to 1, 0 to 10, 0 to 100, and 0 to 1,000 volts. The input resistance on the 0 to 1 volt range is 920K; on the higher ranges the input resistance varies from 9.1 to 10.1 megohms.

The AC voltage ranges are 0 to 5, 0 to 50, 0 to 500, and 0 to 5,000 volts, with the 0 to 5 volt range having an input resistance of 650K, and the higher ranges vary from 1.75 megohms to 1.85 megohms.

Four resistance ranges are provided, the lowest is 0 to 10K ohms, and the highest is 0 to 10 megohms. The center-scale resistance on the lowest range is approximately 100 ohms, and on the highest range it is approximately 100,000 ohms.

The frequency response is ±1 db for 10 cps to 500 kc. The source of power is three size-D cells for the amplifier circuit and one size-C cell for the ohmmeter circuit. The average life of the batteries, which are soldered in the circuit to reduce contact resistance and increase reliability, is specified as 1,000 hours for intermittent operation. The weight of the instrument of Fig. 9-1 is 4.5 pounds, including the batteries. No provision is included for operation from the AC line.

The simplified circuit of the transistorized voltmeter of Fig. 9-1 is shown in Fig. 9-2, and the actual circuit is shown

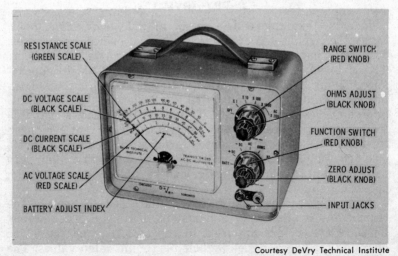

RESISTANCE SCALE (GREEN SCALE)

DC VOLTAGE SCALE (BLACK SCALE)

DC CURRENT SCALE (BLACK SCALE)

AC VOLTAGE SCALE (RED SCALE)

BATTERY ADJUST INDEX

RANGE SWITCH (RED KNOB)

OHMS ADJUST (BLACK KNOB)

FUNCTION SWITCH (RED KNOB)

ZERO ADJUST (BLACK KNOB)

INPUT JACKS

Courtesy DeVry Technical Institute

Fig. 9-1. DeVry TRVM-1 transistorized multimeter.

in Fig. 9-3. The input silicon transistors, Q1 and Q3 require only several microamperes of current for operation, and the total current required by the instrument is approximately 6 milliamperes.

The meter is located in a bridge circuit that includes transistors Q2 and Q4. The potentiometer in series with the 4.5-volt battery supply (Fig. 9-3) is used to compensate for aging of the batteries. To set this, the function switch is turned to the Batt position, and the range switch to the Off position—the pointer should stop near the center of the Batt Adj scale on

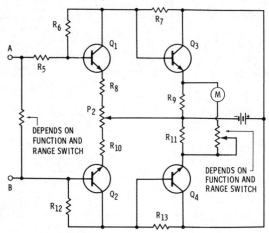

Fig. 9-2. Simplified amplifier schematic of DeVry TRVM-1.

the meter face, which can be seen in the middle of the scale (Fig. 9-1). If it does not, potentiometer P3 is adjusted through a hole in the rear panel until the pointer is in the Middle of the Batt Adj scale designation. If the pointer cannot be centered the batteries should be replaced.

The transistorized meter just considered is classified as being burnout-proof in all its measuring functions, except for the multiplier resistors which could be damaged from severe overload.

LABORATORY INSTRUMENTS

In the final section of this book typical laboratory, precision, or special-purpose instruments must be covered. Those selected are either models now in wide use or new models which, because of new circuits or features, should be indicative of trends in instrument design.

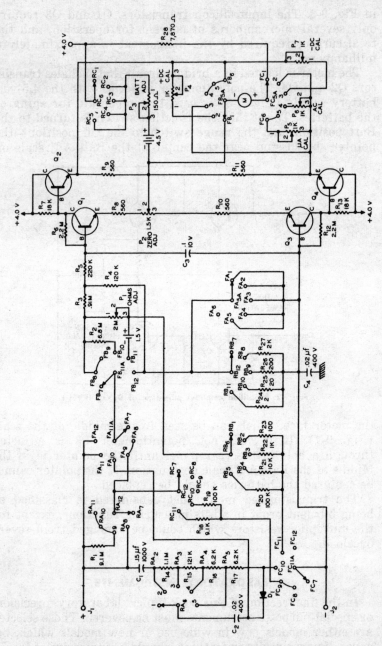

Courtesy DeVry Technical Institute

Fig. 9-3. Complete schematic of DeVry TRVM-1.

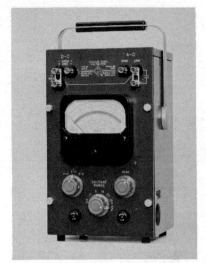

Fig. 9-4. Laboratory VTVM, General Radio 1800-B.

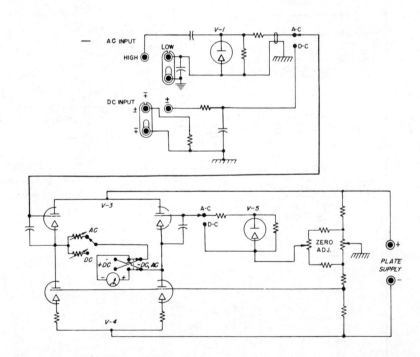

Fig. 9-5. Simplified schematic of General Radio 1800-B VTVM.

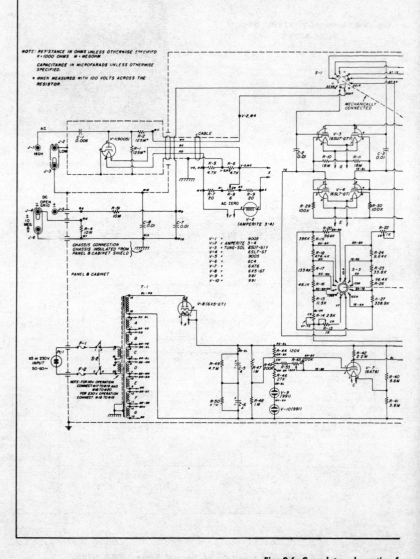

Fig. 9-6. Complete schematic of

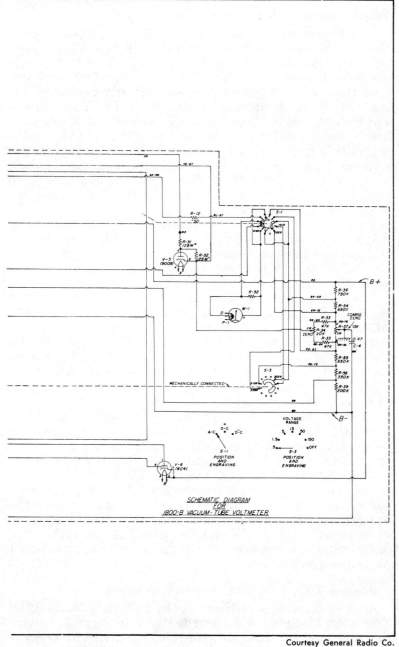

SCHEMATIC DIAGRAM
FOR
1800-B VACUUM-TUBE VOLTMETER

General Radio 1800-B VTVM.

127

General Radio 1800B VTVM

One instrument frequently used in certain applications is the General Radio 1800B VTVM, shown in Fig. 9-4. Probably the major feature of this instrument, aside from its accuracy and reliability, is that it is useful for measuring AC voltages with frequencies to 500 mc. The accuracy is 2 percent of full scale on 12 voltage ranges, six AC ranges and 6 DC ranges. For both AC and DC these six ranges cover 0 to 150 volts. For lower frequencies the input resistance is 25 megohms. for the higher frequencies, the input impedance is somewhat lower due to input capacitance; however, the input capacitance is held to very low values. A shielded diode probe employing an acorn tube, a coaxial fitting, and a coaxial termination is provided with the instrument.

A simplified diagram of the 1800B VTVM is shown in Fig. 9-5, and a complete schematic is shown in Fig. 9-6. The circuit includes function switch S1 and range switch S3 and associated circuits, a DC amplifier, the indicating meter, a degeneration circuit, and a regulated power-supply.

The DC amplifier consists of V3, a balanced dual triode (type 6SU7), operating in a highly degenerated circuit. The rectified AC voltage (or the DC voltage) being measured is applied to the control-grid, pin 1 of V3. A diode (V5), which balances the effect of the initial voltage of rectifier diode V1, is connected to the control-grid, pin 4 of the second triode of the 6SU7. A 100-microampere meter is connected between the cathodes of the two triodes.

On the higher voltage ranges, heavy feedback is introduced in the DC amplifier circuit; on the lower voltage ranges, the feedback is less. This feedback, or degeneration, is obtained by connection of a 6SL7 degeneration triode (V4) in series with the cathode of each DC amplifier triode.

The power supply, which includes transformer T1, and rectifier V8 (type 6X5), is stabilized by two small neon tubes (type 991) V9 and V10, which are followed by an electronic regulator circuit consisting of vacuum-tube types 6C4 and 6AT6. The diode heater voltages are also stabilized by a ballast tube, an Amperite type 3-4.

Ballantine 320A True RMS Electronic Voltmeter

Another laboratory instrument, the Ballantine Model 320A True RMS Electronic Voltmeter is shown in Fig. 9-7. As was mentioned several times previously in this book, the conventional VOM and VTVM respond to either average or peak

Fig. 9-7. Ballantine Model 320A True RMS
electronic voltmeter.

values of a measured voltage or current, but for AC the meters
are calibrated to read rms values. If the voltage being measured is not a true sine wave; the rms value indicated is probably erroneous. The instrument shown here was specifically
designed to indicate true rms values for various types of waveforms over the frequency range of 5 cps to 4 mc. The voltage
ranges provide maximum scale indication between 100 microvolts for the lowest range and 330 volts for the highest range.
The types of waveforms for which rms values are indicated
include sine, complex, pulse, and random.

A special feature of the 320A is that the voltage readings
are made on logarithmic scales. This makes it possible to obtain the same accuracy as the rated 2 percent full-scale accuracy for any reading on these scales. A graph, Fig. 9-8,
provided by the manufacturer, shows how accuracy varies
with percentage of full-scale deflection for a standard linearly-
calibrated meter, as compared with the accuracy for a log-
arithmically-calibrated meter.

The 320A Electronic Voltmeter may also be used as a null
detector (to indicate dips, as in adjustment of oscillators, tuned
circuits, bridges, etc.), down to 10 microvolts. It may also be
used as a wideband amplifier for providing up to 50 rms volts

output. Another feature is that an output current is proportional to the mean-square value of the input voltage. The current output can be used to drive a recorder or other readout device.

The applications of this instrument include the following, as suggested by Ballantine:

General rms voltage measurement in grounded circuits.

Noise figure determination of tubes, transistors, networks and resistors.

True rms vibration measurements, in conjunction with vibration pickup.

White noise tests of audio equipment and noise level checks in wide-band carrier and video systems.

Mean-square, sound-pressure measurement and acoustic studies with suitable microphones.

As audio output power-meter with appropriate load impedance.

Measurement of total harmonic distortion in conjunction with a fundamental suppression filter.

The circuit of the Ballantine 320A True RMS Voltmeter is rather complex. It is shown in simplified form in Fig. 9-9. The main features are an Input and a Midsection Attenuator which affect the voltmeter sensitivity on all ranges except the 0.3 microvolt range. On this range the input voltage amplitude is

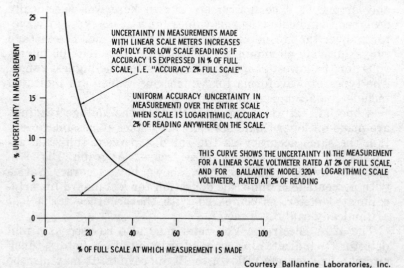

Courtesy Ballantine Laboratories, Inc.

Fig. 9-8. Graph comparing accuracy of linear scale with Ballantine logarithmic scale.

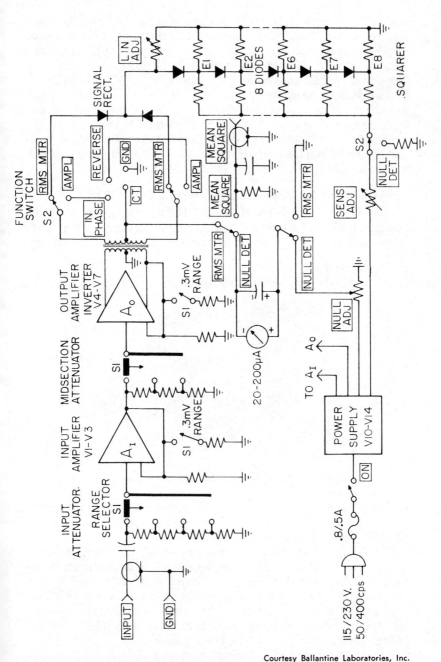

Courtesy Ballantine Laboratories, Inc.

Fig. 9-9. Simplified circuit diagram of Ballantine 320A.

increased in amplitude. A three-stage input amplifier having a gain of 135 with 42 db of feedback (on the 0.3 microvolt range the gain is increased to 240); a three-stage output amplifier, with a gain of 38 and approximately 38 db of feedback (on the 0.3 microvolt range the gain increases to 67) are included. A two-stage phase-inverter for driving the push-pull output transformer and a carefully designed square-law detector circuit complete the circuit. A full explanation of this circuit, the schematic, the operation of the instrument, and detailed descriptions of various applications are included in the instruction manual.

Transistorized AC Voltmeter, Hewlett-Packard 403B

The Hewlett-Packard Model 403B transistorized AC voltmeter, an all-transistor AC voltmeter, is designed for general purpose use (Fig. 9-10). It is particularly useful in labora-

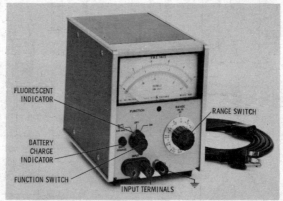

Courtesy Hewlett-Packard Co.

Fig. 9-10. HP 403B transistorized AC voltmeter.

tories, production-line testing and accurate field measurement. This model, weighing 6.5 pounds, replaces an earlier version, the 403A, which is also all-transistorized.

The instrument utilizes a fuse-protected, taut-band-suspension meter movement. It can measure AC voltages from 5 cps to 2 mc, between 100 microvolts and 300 volts, and it can operate either from internal batteries or from the AC 115/230-volt 50 cps to 100 cps line. The batteries are automatically recharged during AC operation, and their condition may be checked with a switch on the front panel.

Available accessories include optional alligator or probe-alligator clips, a 10:1, 10-megohm divider probe, a line-

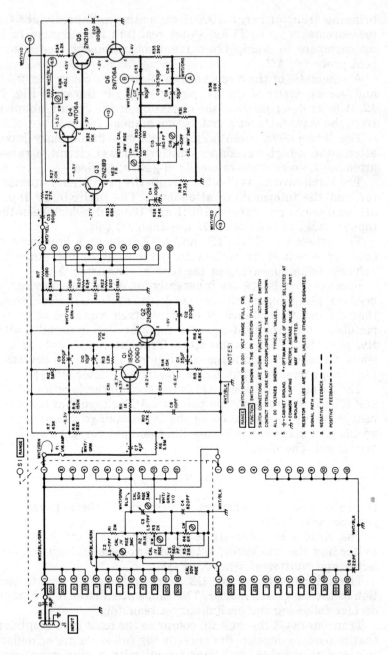

Courtesy Hewlett-Packard Co.

Fig. 9-11. Schematic of HP model 403B.

bridging transformer, a 1000:1 capacitive voltage divider for measurements up to 25 kv, shunt resistors for adaption to 1-microampere to 3-amperes current measurement, and a current probe for AC.

A schematic of the circuit of the 403B is shown in Fig. 9-11, and the schematic of the AC power supply is shown in Fig. 9-12. A brief description of the operation of the circuit, adapted from the manufacturer's instruction manual, follows.

The Model 403B essentially consists of a preliminary input attenuator, a high impedance emitter follower circuit, a range attenuator, and a wide-range, fixed-gain amplifier.

The Range switch is divided up into the preliminary attenuator and the intermediate attenuator. The preliminary input attenuator has two ranges, 100:1 and 10,000:1, which keep the input voltage to transistor Q1 less than .03 volt.

The network of R11, CR1, and CR2 make up a limiting circuit for overload protection to prevent high instantaneous voltages from appearing at the base of transistor Q1.

Because transistors are inherently low-impedance devices, a need for a high input-impedance (Z_i) is required. It would seem that the input resistance of the first stage would be approximately R_i of a grounded-collector configuration in parallel with R9, plus the R7-R8 combination. Transistors Q1 and Q2 are emitter followers exhibiting unity gain and no phase reversal. (R_i = approximate input Z of a common-collector stage).

The output of transistor Q2 is fed back to the junction of R9 and R7-R8. There is at this point an AC voltage that has very nearly the same amplitude as the input voltage. Since a very small AC voltage exists across R9, the input current I_{in} will be very small. Thereby:

$$Z_{in} = \frac{E_{in}}{I_{in}}$$

It can be seen that when I_{in} is very small, the apparent Z_{in} becomes very large.

The R_i of transistor Q1 is increased in a similar manner by feeding the transistor, Q2 emitter voltage to both the collector and emitter of transistor Q1.

The output of transistor Q2 is fed to the intermediate section of the range attenuator. The range attenuator is a voltage divider following the preliminary attenuator.

Transistors Q3 through Q6 comprise the fixed-gain amplifier that is used to develop the current for full-scale meter deflection and to provide the meter circuit with a high-impedance source for linear operation at all current levels.

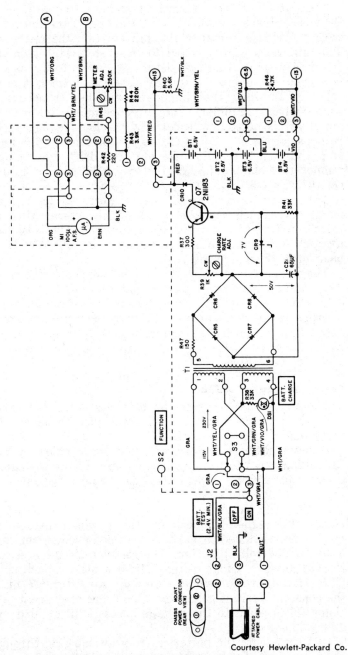

Courtesy Hewlett-Packard Co.

Fig. 9-12. Power supply schematic of HP model 403B.

The output of the intermediate-range attenuator is fed to the base of transistor Q3 (differential amplifier) and compared with a feedback signal to its emitter from the meter circuit. This difference signal is fed to transistor Q4, which in turn is directly coupled to transistors Q5 and Q6. Transistor Q4 is a grounded-emitter amplifier. Transistor Q5 is a common-collector amplifier that impedance-matches transistor Q6, a common-base amplifier. The direct-coupling feature of the amplifiers is necessary because of the low-frequency (5 cps) response of the 403B. R24 through R26 form the DC feedback loop that tends to minimize any DC drift due to ambient temperature change. R33 corrects the total gain of transistors Q3 through Q6.

The meter source impedance is increased by the use of negative feedback from the output of the meter rectifier bridge to the emitter of the differential amplifier, Q3. Resistor R28 through R30, and C15 and C16 correct the phase of the feedback at high frequencies.

The meter rectifier circuit is a bridge-type with a crystal diode and a capacitor in each branch and a DC microammeter connected across its midpoints. The current through the meter is proportional to the average value of the input voltage waveform. Calibration of the meter in rms volts is based on the ratio that exists between the average and effective values of a sine-wave voltage.

Power Supply HP 403B

The Model 403B operates on batteries only; these are four 6.5-volt nickel cadmium batteries designed to have a life of forty hours before recharging.

Resistor R-39 is factory adjusted for a charging rate of 11 milliamperes to prolong battery life. If the instrument is used frequently in the field, R-39 can be adjusted for a charging rate of 20 milliamperes.

In Fig. 9-12 the AC battery-charging power supply is illustrated. For 115-volt operation the power-transformer primaries are switched in parallel, and switched in series when used for 230-volt operation. The rectifier circuit is a conventional full-wave bridge using C21 for a filter capacitor. Diode CR9 (7-volt breakdown diode) and transistor Q7 make up the constant current generator. The collector current of transistor Q7 is equal to the voltage across CR9 divided by R37 and R39.

CR10 prevents the batteries from discharging through the charging circuit when the instrument is in the Off position.

HP 410C Electronic Voltmeter

The Hewlett-Packard 410C Electronic Voltmeter, shown in Fig. 9-13 is a transistorized version of the 410B that has been widely used in electrical measurement work as a general purpose instrument. A brief description of the 410C is included here.

This instrument measures DC voltages from 1.5 millivolts to 1,500 volts and direct current from 0.15 nanoamperes (.15 × 10⁻⁹ amperes) to 150 ma. Resistance is measured from

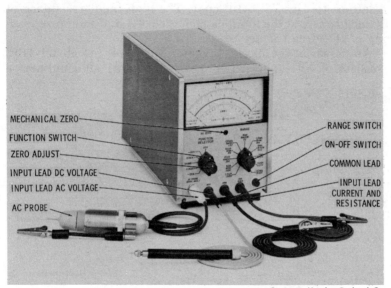

MECHANICAL ZERO
FUNCTION SWITCH
ZERO ADJUST
INPUT LEAD DC VOLTAGE
INPUT LEAD AC VOLTAGE
AC PROBE

RANGE SWITCH
ON-OFF SWITCH
COMMON LEAD
INPUT LEAD CURRENT AND RESISTANCE

Courtesy Hewlett-Packard Co.

Fig. 9-13. HP 410C electronic voltmeter.

0.2 ohm to 500 megohms. With an optional plug-in probe, AC voltages can be measured, at 20 cps to 700 mc, from 50 microvolts to 300 volts. These measurements are made with laboratory precision. The Model 410C uses a Hewlett-Packard photoconductor chopper-amplifier, a hybrid circuit combining the best features of a vacuum tube and two transistors. This hybrid circuit makes possible a high input impedance. The impedance is 100 megohms on the DC voltmeter and the low-resistance (less than 3 ohms) recorder output. The chopper-stabilized amplifier eliminates the need for a zero adjustment on the direct current, DC voltage and resistance ranges. Additionally, no adjustment for infinite resistance is needed. Elimination of these zero controls simplifies operation. A high sensitivity, low-drift, and low-noise neon oscillator in addition to the photoconductor chopper-amplifier makes the 410C suitable as a preamplifier for data recording on analog recorders. The 410C has several self-protective features incorporated. Even when overloaded at up to 100 times full-scale (40 db), it will recover in less than three seconds.

With an optional AC probe, the 410C will measure AC voltages with 3 percent accuracy over a range of 100 cps to 100 mc. This special probe permits measurements of 10 percent accuracy from 20 cps to 700 mc and will produce comparative indications to 3 gc (3×10^9 cps). The high input resistance of 10 megohms and the input capacitance of 1.5 pf minimize loading of the circuit under test.

As shown in the block diagram, Fig. 9-14, the Model 410C consists of an input network, a modulator, an amplifier, a

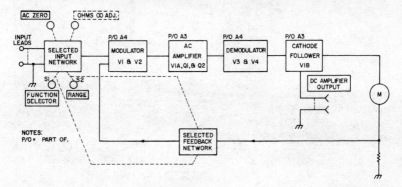

Courtesy Hewlett-Packard Co.

Fig. 9-14. Block diagram of HP 410C electronic voltmeter.

demodulator, and a meter circuit. The voltmeter circuits and the front and rear panel controls and connectors associated with them are shown. Signals to be measured are applied through the appropriate input lead to the input network. AC voltages are detected in the AC probe, and therefore all signals to the input network are DC. The input network attenuates the DC signal to a level determined by the Range and Function Selector settings. The attenuated DC voltage is applied to the modulator that converts the attenuated DC voltage to AC voltage for amplification. The amplified AC signal is converted back to DC voltage in the demodulator and coupled to the cathode follower (V1B. The cathode follower output to the DC Amplifier Output connector and meter circuit is a DC voltage proportional to the amplitude of the signal applied to the input. A portion of the voltage to the meter circuit is returned to the modulator as feedback. The feedback is a voltage proportional to the meter indication. When the feedback voltage and attenuated DC voltage are nearly equal, the meter stabilizes.

Index

Principle of meter movement, 17, 18
Probes, 37
  high-voltage, 40, 41, 42
  VTVM, 89-91

R

Range indicating VOM, 46-48
Rectifier replacement, 78, 79
RCA Senior VoltOhmyst VTVM, 99-104
Rectifier tests, forward-reverse, 66, 67
Relationship of voltage, current, and resistance, 12-15
Removal of VOM from case, 76, 77
Repeatability, 57
Replacement
  fuse, 77
  rectifier, 78, 79
  resistors, 79, 80
Resistance
  definition of, 12
  measurement, 62, 63
    basic VOM circuits for, 25-27
  VTVM, 87, 88
Resistor replacement, 79, 80
Resistors, 12, 13, 14
Resistors used in VOM's, 42
Response, frequency, 56, 57
Review of electricity, 9-15

S

Schematic of General Radio 1800-B, 125-127
Schematic of Sencore SM112, 118
Sencore SM112 combination VOM-VTVM, 117-120

Sensitive circuits, measurements in, 71, 72
Sensitivity, 52, 53
  VOM, 31, 32
Soldering connections in VOM, 80
Special applications of VTVM, 114-116
Specifications, 52-58
Static charge, erratic readings due to, 117
Switches, 42, 43

T

Table, correction factor $10 \log \dfrac{600}{R}$, 108
Taut-band suspension meter movement, 35, 36
Testing
  batteries, 70, 71
  electronic circuits, 70
  fused circuits, 67, 68
  meter movement, 77, 78
Test leads, 37-42
Tracking, 57
Transistorized AC voltmeter, Hewlett-Packard 403B, 132-136
Transistorized electronic voltmeters, 121-123
Triplett Model 850 VTVM, 105, 106
Trouble chart for typical combination VOM-VTVM, 119, 120
True rms electronic voltmeter, applications of, 130
Typical VTVM circuit, 92-94

The Consolation of Otherness